A History of the
Radcliffe Observatory
Oxford

The Radcliffe Observatory, etching by Irvine Loudon RE, 2000

A History of the Radcliffe Observatory Oxford

The Biography of a Building

Edited by Jeffery Burley and Kristina Plenderleith

with contributions from

Jeffery Burley

Roger Hutchins

Peter Inskip

Irvine Loudon

Michael Pirie

Michael Popkin

Terence Ryan

Geoffrey Tyack

Gordon Wallace

Published by
Green College at the Radcliffe Observatory
Woodstock Road, Oxford, OX2 6HG

ISBN: 0-9509394-1-2

First published 2005

Produced for the publishers by
Robert Boyd, Printing & Publishing Services
260 Colwell Drive, Witney, Oxon, OX28 5LW

Printed and bound by the Alden Group
Osney Mead, Oxford, OX2 0EF

Contents

Illustrations

Profiles of the authors and editors

Jeffery Burley obtained an undergraduate degree in forestry at Oxford University in 1961 and completed a doctorate at Yale University in 1965 in forest genetics. His final professional post was as Professor of Forestry and Director of the Oxford Forestry Institute. In parallel he was Vice-Warden of Green College where he is now Development Fellow.

Roger Hutchins obtained his undergraduate degree at Oxford University and completed his doctorate there in 1999 on a comparative and thematic analysis of six British University Observatories. Roger Hutchins directs the Development Office at Magdalen College.

Peter Inskip is director in charge of historic buildings work at Peter Inskip + Peter Jenkins Architects. His principal works include the restoration of the Albert Memorial, Somerset House and Waddesdon Manor. His interest in the relationship of buildings to their setting resulted in his involvement with the restoration of Stowe, the greatest English landscape garden. He taught architecture at Cambridge for ten years and has served on the advisory committees of the National Trust, the Heritage Lottery Fund, English Heritage and the World Monuments Fund.

Irvine Loudon is an Honorary Associate of the Wellcome Unit for the History of Medicine and Honorary Fellow of Green College. He is a medical historian whose career included working as house-physician and house surgeon and in general practice. He is also an etcher and Member of the Council of the Royal Society of Painter-Printmakers.

Michael Pirie has worked as head gardener at Green College, Oxford University, since 1980. He is a tutor in garden history at Oxford University's Department for Continuing Education, and works with summer schools in Oxford.

Kristina Plenderleith took an undergraduate degree in geography at University College, London and a master's degree in forestry at Oxford University. She has edited a range of books on environmental, social and scientific topics.

Michael Popkin is a language graduate from Cambridge University. He took a PGCE from London University before joining HM Overseas Civil Service in 1947. Returning to England in 1964, Michael Popkin was employed at the Oxford Polytechnic, where his main interests were in educational methods.

Terence Ryan was Professor of Dermatology in Oxford University, President of the International Dermatological Association and Chairman of Oxford Medical Alumni and the Friends of 13 Norham Gardens (Sir William Osler's home while he was Professor of Medicine) up to his retirement in 2000. He was formerly Vice-Warden of Green College.

Geoffrey Tyack has an undergraduate degree in history and a M.Litt. degree in architectural history from Oxford University. He completed a doctorate at London University. His main academic interests are in British and European architectural history and the history of urban planning since the Renaissance.

Gordon Wallace graduated from the Universities of Glasgow (English and History) and Oxford (Geography). Retiring early from HM Diplomatic Service in 1980 he took up a teaching appointment in Oxford where, through his friendship with CG Smith, Director of the Radcliffe Meteorological Station 1950-87, he wrote *Meteorological Observations at the Radcliffe Observatory Oxford: 1815-1995.*

Foreword

This is a surprising, informative and amusing book. It is surprising because, excluding encyclopaedias, not many books cover such a wide range of apparently disparate subjects (ranging from architecture and antiquity through garden design, astronomy and meteorology, to medical research and the life of an Oxford college). It is informative because it provides, to a high academic standard, factual, historical information about these subjects, the relevant activities within and around the Radcliffe Observatory building, and the key persons who influenced the design, construction, maintenance, management and use of the building. It is amusing in demonstrating some of their personal idiosyncracies and impacts while working within the framework of an ancient University.

The book is essentially a biography of the building and reflects its existence as the living organism that it has been for over two centuries. Different owners, occupiers and activities necessitated changes to the internal structures but the external structure has remained constant as the home for them all and as the dominant architectural feature of the northern part of the University's area. Regrettably the ravages of the weather and environmental pollution damaged the exterior to such an extent that a major programme of restoration was initiated in 2003 (and we hope that the sales of this book will contribute in a small way to offset the substantial costs of this restoration).

By the year 2005 Green College has occupied the building for only 25 of its 225 years but the coincidence of the two anniversaries with the period of restoration seems an appropriate time to review the history of the Observatory and its associated buildings and grounds. The editors have sought to maintain the individual style of the authors of individual chapters of the book who are needless to say, specialists in their subjects. They have also selected illustrations that have a wide artistic and historical appeal. Each chapter is supported by a number of end notes providing links to further specialized reference material and there is a common bibliography at the end of the book that provides the major, easily accessible, reference books.

Personally I would like to thank the authors and my co-editor for their extremely generous contributions of time and intellectual effort to make the book interesting and stimulating to a wide audience. Kristin Plenderleith, Irvine Loudon and Michael Pirie were particularly helpful and I also acknowledge reviews of chapters by Charles Barclay and Richard Washington. We thank Bob Boyd for his admirable advice and service as the printer of this volume. We all hope that it will stimulate the present and future generations of both College members and wider public to know and understand the life story of a fascinating building that is a major component of the national heritage.

Professor Jeffery Burley
Senior Editor and
Development Fellow, Green College

1 June 2005

Preface

We have had the privilege and pleasure of leading Green College as its Wardens throughout its first quarter of a century. Although one of the youngest colleges of the University of Oxford, Green College is fortunate to occupy the Radcliffe Observatory, one of the older and most beautiful buildings in the city. The building was created for astronomical observation but it has also been used for a range of other activities since its opening. These activities are reviewed in separate chapters; they provide historical facts and interesting views on personalities concerned with the creation and management of the building throughout its 225 years of existence.

As the latest and current owner-occupier of the Radcliffe Observatory, Green College provides academic, administrative and social support for graduate students and Fellows in a relatively narrow range of scientific disciplines, many of which continue some of the classical ideas and previous interests practised within the Observatory building. The College owns and occupies several other buildings but the Radcliffe Observatory is the heart of the institution and the College is responsible for its maintenance for the benefit of the members of the College, the public and the national heritage.

We are delighted to endorse the production of this book that reviews the history of the Observatory and that may raise funds for the restoration of the building. The authors and editors of the book have generously allocated their considerable time and financial interest in the book to Green College; a number of individual members and friends of the College have kindly sponsored the publication. To all of these we extend our sincere thanks and we commend the book to a wide-ranging audience interested in the diversity of subjects it covers.

Sir Richard Doll, Lord Walton of Detchant, Dr Trevor Hughes, Sir Crispin Tickell and Sir John Hanson.

1 June 2005

Acknowledgements

The editors and authors are grateful to the following institutions and people for direct help and for permission to reproduce original illustrations:-

The Radcliffe Trust; the Bodleian Library, Oxford; the Ashmolean Museum, Oxford; the Centre for Oxfordshire Studies; Country Life Picture Library; The Times; Dr Jon Whiteley and the staff of the print room of the Ashmolean Museum, Oxford; Michael Stansfield, archivist at Corpus Christi College, Oxford; the Fellow Archivist of St John's College, Dr Malcolm Vale, and his assistant Mark Pridday; Colin Harris of the Modern Papers Reading Room, Bodleian Library; Sharan Attar, Development Officer, and Jane Rogers, Development Director, Green College; Charles Barclay, Director of the Blackett Observatory, Marlborough College; Gwen Barer; Sir Richard Doll; Maureen Forrest; Sir Graham Liggins; Bill Lund; Heather Shelley (nee Hooton); Wilbur Wright; Derek Wyatt.

Modern photographs were supplied by Peter Inskip, Peter Jenkins, Jeffery Burley, Andrew Markus and Geoffrey Tyack.

Sponsors

The Warden, Fellows and Members of Green College acknowledge with grateful thanks the generous support of the following for the costs of producing this volume:

Mr Robert Barrington
Professor Shouma Bhattacharya
Dr Colin C F Blake
Dr Max Blythe
Sir Walter Bodmer
Mr Matthijs Branderhorst
Dr & Mrs Paul Brankin
Dr Angela Brueggemann
Mr Peter Burge
Dr Susan Burge
Professor and Mrs Jeffery Burley
Sir John Burnett
Ms Lindy Castell
Professor Donald A Chambers
Mr Paddy Coulter
Sir Richard Doll
Professor Alan Emery
Mr Jeremy Fairbank
Dr K A Fleming
Dr E W L Fletcher
Professor & Mrs Keith Frayn
Professor Hugh Freeman
Professor Peter Friend
Dr William C Gibson
Professor Sir John and
    Dr Lady Corinne Grimley-Evans
Professor Clive Hahn
Sir John Hanson
Dr Peter Holland
Dr John Horder
Dr Elisabeth Hsu
Dr J Trevor Hughes
Dr R Hutchins
Professor Derek Jewell
Dr Fumiko Kawasaki
Dr John Kerr

Mr & Mrs Ian Laing
Dr John Lennox
Dr Irvine Loudon
Professor James Lovelock
Dr Michael Lockwood
Dr Andrew Markus
Mr P Michael Mason
Professor & Mrs Yoshio Maya
Dr John McGovern
Dr Mary McMenamin
Dr Ann McPherson
Dr Gerald Myatt
Dr Douglas Noble
Professor John O'Connor
Dr G M C Paterson
Mr Lindsay A Pirie
Professor Richard Pring
Professor Stewart Purvis
Mr John Raisman
Professor Kenneth B M Reid
Professor and Mrs Terence J Ryan
Professor Tamaki Sasaki
Professor John Sear
Dr J B Selkon
Dr Rebecca Surrender
Professor Sir Keith Sykes
Sir Crispin Tickell
Mr Colin Tudge
Dr Jennie Turner
Dr Martin Turner
Professor Geoffrey Walford
Mr Brian Walker
Lord Walton of Detchant
Professor John Wass
Professor Stephen Woolgar

Green College also gratefully acknowledges the generous support of the following together with the many individual members and friends of the College for the restoration of the Observatory:

The Pilgrim Trust
The Oxford Preservation Trust
The Idlewild Trust
Sir Richard Doll
The Wolfson Foundation
The Headley Trust
The Patrick Trust
The Alan Evans Memorial Trust

The Thriplow Charitable Trust
The Lord Barnby's Foundation
The J Paul Getty Jr Charitable Trust
The P F Charitable Trust
The Leche Trust
The Garfield Weston Foundation
The Girdlers' Company
The Bernard Sunley Charitable Foundation

Chapter 1

The Making of the Radcliffe Observatory[1]

Geoffrey Tyack

According to the seventeenth century antiquary Anthony Wood, the first observatory in Oxford was the ancient medieval gatehouse known as Friar Bacon's Study, guarding the southern approach to the city at Folly Bridge; here, according to legend, the Friar 'did sometimes use the night season to ascend this place ... and there to take the altitude and distance of the stars.'[2] However, the recorded, as opposed to the mythical, history of observatories in Oxford begins with the foundation of the Savilian Professorship of Astronomy in 1619. No purpose-built observatory was supplied by the University but the first Professor, John Bainbridge, was allowed to use the top room of the gate tower of the newly erected Schools Quadrangle, completed structurally in the very year of the foundation of the professorship. And here Bainbridge's successor John Greaves kept his collection of telescopes and other instruments.

The creation of the professorship came just before the first observatories designed for telescopes were erected.[3] Hans Lippersky of Middelburg, a lens-maker, presented what is reckoned to be the first telescope to the States General of Holland in 1608, and in 1632-3 an observatory was built on the roof of the University of Leiden, followed by others at Utrecht and elsewhere, including one built by

King Christian IV of Denmark in 1637-42 in the form of an 118 foot high tower attached to the church of Holy Trinity, Copenhagen.[4] The first European observatories were not very sophisticated buildings but in 1667 Claude Perrault, himself a scientist though not an astronomer, designed a more elaborate observatory at Paris which still survives in an altered form; it was a two storeyed structure with a flat roof, projections at the corners for the telescopes, a room for larger astronomical instruments, and a meeting room for the members of Colbert's recently established Académie des Sciences. Then in 1675 the Royal Observatory was built at Greenwich to the designs of Christopher Wren, who held the Savilian chair in Oxford from 1661 to 1673. It contained an octagonal observing room for movable telescopes, rooms on either side for the fixed instruments, and lodgings for the Astronomer Royal, who needed to be on hand in order to make night-time observations; the longer telescopes, including one of 123 feet, were mounted on poles in the garden.

There is no indication that Wren ever intended an observatory of this kind for Oxford, and, in a letter to John Fell, Dean of Christ Church, Oxford, on 8 December 1681, he said that an adequate observatory could be placed 'as well in a garden as a tower' and need consist of no more than a 'little house of boards' 12 foot square and 7 foot high with a detachable roof;[5] it could house a telescope, a mural quadrant and a 'quadrant to take distances'. Such a utilitarian structure was in fact built in 1705 by the then Savilian Professor, Edmund Halley, on the roof of his official residence in New College Lane, where it can still be seen.[6] It was presumably adequate for observations made through smaller telescopes but James Bradley, who succeeded Halley in 1721, complained that there were not enough instruments in Oxford to enable him to carry out his research properly, or a building capable of housing his own instruments, which included a 15 foot telescope.[7] His successor, Thomas Hornsby, solved the problem temporarily by creating an observatory of his own at Corpus Christi College, but this was clearly no more than a stop-gap solution, and in 1768 he petitioned the Radcliffe Trustees for money to build a proper observatory out of the interest on the property left to Oxford University in 1714 by the physician John Radcliffe.[8] This gift – one of the most generous in Oxford's history – had already enabled the construction of James Gibbs's magnificent Radcliffe Library (now known as the Radcliffe Camera) and, more recently, the Radcliffe Infirmary, a much plainer building of 1759-67 by the Eton builder Stiff Leadbetter.[9] It now enabled the University to erect, at no cost to itself, the finest of all eighteenth century observatories.[10]

In his initial letter to the Radcliffe Trustees, Hornsby set out his requirements for the building.[11] There should first of all be a building at ground level for the larger instruments which, in his own words, 'must be placed on the ground and fixed to the plane of the meridian'; they comprised quadrants, a zenith sector (a long telescope fixed to a wall and pointing out of a roof) and a transit instrument (a revolving telescope), all of which were needed to measure the position

and movements of the heavenly bodies – seen then as a prime task of astronomy, mainly for its value in assisting navigation. The instruments had to be fixed to piers firmly embedded into the ground in order to minimize movement, and they had to be aligned with the meridian so as to supply a fixed line from which observations could begin. So the building had to be a single storeyed structure aligned, like the Paris observatory, on an east–west axis. Also, since some of the instruments rotated on an arc of 180 degrees, there had to be shutter openings in the walls and roof. Hornsby also requested a 'large room for experimental philosophy' which he suggested might be placed over his new official residence; above it there would be another room of the same size for 'occasional observations in any part of the Heavens', housing the movable refracting telescopes used for such observations.[12] This implied the building of a three storeyed tower observatory, perhaps not unlike that built at Berlin in 1706,[13] as well as a lower adjacent building for the large instruments. The total cost, including the ground and the instruments was estimated by Hornsby at £6,000 or £7,000, a sum which was to be greatly exceeded.

The first step towards the construction of the new observatory took place in 1771, when the Trustees resolved to ask the Lord Chancellor for permission to use the Radcliffe funds to buy 'a piece of ground and to erect thereon a large Observatory Room for the use of the Savilian Professor of Astronomy to read courses of lectures; and to purchase such mathematical instruments as are proper to be used there.'[14] The ground was to the north of the city's built-up area, alongside the road to Woodstock and beyond the Infirmary (Plate 1, p. 11). It had been leased from St John's College in 1770 by the Fourth Duke of Marlborough, an enthusiast for astronomy.[15]

Permission was granted, and designs procured from Henry Keene, an architect much favoured by Oxford University in the previous decade, with work at Christ Church, University College and Balliol College to his credit.[16] The Professor's official lodgings were now to be placed in a separate house away from the main structure, which would be devoted entirely to scientific research and teaching, and the cost was estimated upwards to £11,381, including £2,500 for astronomical instruments, which were, in the event, paid for out of a windfall from the Clarendon Press.[17] Keene met the Radcliffe Trustees on 31 January 1772, and on 16 March showed them his designs, which do not appear to have survived; the foundation stone was laid in June of the same year.[18]

Keene's appointment may have come about through the influence of the Third Earl of Lichfield, Chairman of the Radcliffe Trustees and Chancellor of the University, and it was Keene who designed Lord Lichfield's impressive monument in Spelsbury church, near his country seat at Ditchley (Oxfordshire). When Lichfield died on 19 September 1772 he was replaced, both as Chairman of the Trustees and Chancellor of the University, by another Oxfordshire nobleman, Lord North, of Wroxton Abbey, Member of Parliament for Banbury and Prime Minister since 1770,[19] and in March 1773 the Trustees were shown another elevation for the Observatory, which they approved. Keene was then ordered to give an account of the work already done and told not to proceed further, though he carried on as builder when work resumed.[20] The second elevation must have been by James Wyatt, who was paid £100 by the Trustees in 1774, and when Keene died in 1776 his son Theodosius was told to finish the building under Wyatt's direction.[21]

The reason for the change of architect is not entirely clear. There may have been some lobbying by Sir William Bagot of Blithfield (Staffordshire), one of the Trustees and the head of the family which had financed Wyatt's

journey to Italy in the 1760s.[22] There also seems to have been a feeling that Keene's design was too plain for a major public building in (or on the edge of) a city of grandiose architectural monuments. The architectural improvement of Oxford was a subject of public interest in the 1770s, after the recent passing of a Paving Act (1766) which led to the demolition of the old east and north gates, the building of a new market, and of the new Magdalen Bridge carrying the London road over the Cherwell, begun in 1772.[23] In his pamphlet *Oxonia Explicata et Ornata* (1773) Edward Tatham, Rector of Lincoln College and one of the most vociferous of the local cognoscenti, specifically criticized the original design for the Observatory, calling it a 'heavy, sluggish heap', complaining that it was to be placed in a situation where no one could see it, and urging that the new building should 'reflect grandeur and magnificence in Oxford'.[24]

Wyatt's architecture certainly had the merit of boldness and novelty after the tame neo-Palladianism of buildings like the nearby Infirmary. Both the Pantheon assembly room in Oxford Street, London (1772) and Heaton Hall near Manchester, begun at about the same time, showed that he was capable of reinterpreting the classical language of architecture and ornament in an engaging and original way, making him a credible rival to the older and better-established Adam brothers, who built nothing in either of the two ancient English universities. Like the Adams, Wyatt was adept at displacing established architects, and in Oxford the victim was Keene, whom he superseded not only at the Observatory but also at Christ Church, where he built the new Canterbury Quadrangle in 1773-6, and later, after Keene's death, at Worcester College.[25] With the assistance of the builder and carpenter James Pears, Mayor of Oxford in 1794,[26] he went on to dominate the architectural life of the city for the rest of the eighteenth century, designing the library at Oriel College and engaging in numerous restorations of medieval buildings at New College, Magdalen College and elsewhere.[27] Nevertheless, it was the Observatory which made his reputation, and it is this singular building which constitutes his most striking and original architectural contribution to the city.

Since we do not know what Keene's original design looked like[28] we can only infer how much of the present building is his and how much Wyatt's (Plate 4, p. 13). The hipped-roofed parsonage-like Professor's house, into which Hornsby moved with his family in 1773,[29] could easily have been designed by any competent Georgian builder, and the same applies to the stable block which is joined to it by an office wing and which now forms part of the entrance quadrangle at Green College.[30] There is no reason to assume that Wyatt had anything to do with these buildings but the main Observatory is more problematic. According to James Pears' clerk, John Hudson, writing long after the event in 1834, Wyatt 'altered the plan and outside finishing' of the main building, leaving the remainder to be 'carried up by Mr Jas Pears under the direction of Mr James Wyatt and roofed in 1778'.[31] This account seems to be broadly accurate, so long as we assume that the 'main building' referred to one of the single storeyed structures containing the astronomical instruments which were the *raison d'être* of the whole project. They were finished by the summer of 1773, when the astronomical instruments were delivered by the well known London instrument maker, John Bird,[32] and they are shown with the scaffolding not yet removed in a drawing of October 1774 by the local drawing-master John Baptist Malchair (Plate 2, p. 11).[33]

The layout of the two single storeyed buildings can only be understood with reference to the astronomical instruments they were designed to contain (Plate 7, p. 15). The eastern building (the present east wing) was linked by a semicircular corridor to the Professor's house and contained the most important instruments: a transit instrument; two mural quadrants of 8 foot radius, one facing north and the other south; and a 12 foot zenith sector, which was placed in a central north facing room which still retains its wooden gallery. The instruments were mounted on heavy stone piers embedded in concrete to minimize the danger of movement, and could project through slots in the walls and roof, which could be closed with wooden shutters (Plate 8, p. 16).[34] There was also a study for Hornsby. The west wing, externally identical, contained smaller instruments brought to the new building by Hornsby from his old observatory at Corpus Christi College 'for the use and practice of young students'.[35] There was also a detached circular building (since demolished) to the south, containing an equatorial sector, which could scan the heavens in all directions.[36]

Each of the wings has its own entrance, set within a relieving arch, and each is starkly neo-classical in appearance, with a flat, unencumbered roof-line and no balustrade (Plate 9, p. 16). This effect, anticipating Soane's stable block at Chelsea Hospital, was dictated by the need to ensure that the scientific instruments could project out through the slots in the walls and roof – an interesting example of the 'form follows function' dictum; these slots can be clearly seen in early photographs of the north front but they were smoothed over when the building was refaced in 1960-9. Ornament was kept to a minimum, apart from a guilloche moulding at cornice level and Coade stone swags and *paterae* over the windows; this was an early use of this material, which was only patented in 1768.[37] It remains an open question whether Keene was involved in any way in the design of the wings. He was still alive and actively engaged on the building while they were being constructed but his other classical buildings in Oxford, like the almost exactly contemporary Provost's Lodgings at Worcester College (1773-6), show none of the precocious interest in neo-classical form and decoration seen at the Observatory. It seems likely therefore that the facades of the wings are essentially Wyatt's work.

With the wings in use, and Hornsby comfortably ensconced in his new house, the Observatory was in effect operational, and when the Danish astronomer Thomas Bugge visited Hornsby in 1777 he declared that it was 'the best in Europe, both as regards the arrangement and the instruments'. Bugge expected it to be finished in three years,[38] but in fact it took another 22 years to complete the whole project. In February 1776 the Trustees authorized payments of £261 for Headington stone and £50 for Windrush stone (the latter used for the tower), and another of £299 to John Bolton for plumber's work.[39] Construction of the central block was under way by May 1776, when the Trustees resolved to 'finish the Building up to the Second Story'.[40] By then £7,500 had already been spent out of the £11,381 originally estimated, and the Trustees resolved to keep future costs down to an annual £800 to £1,000. A drawing by Malchair, dated 1777 (Plate 3, p. 12), shows the first floor structurally complete and on 27 November the locksmith Thomas Blockley was paid £70 for locks.[41] According to John Hudson, the second-floor tower which crowned the composition was finished in 1778.[42] There matters rested for another ten years: £14,632 had been spent by 1780 – over £1,000 more than the total cost of the Radcliffe Infirmary – but the central block remained an empty shell without any of its proposed external sculpture until the end of the decade. By 1799, when work on the interiors and the external embellishments finally came to an end, the cost had risen to £31,661, nearly three times what had been proposed in 1771.[43]

In his *Cours d'Architecture* (1771) the French architect and theorist J-F. Blondel wrote that an observatory should have a 'decided character' (*un caractère décidé*).[44] Wyatt imparted this elusive quality by adopting a semicircular plan for the central block and by his unconventional use of neo-classical motifs and methods of architectural composition. Viewed from the south, the composition builds up in a jerky, somewhat angular, fashion from the low one storeyed wings though the two storeyed first floor of the central portion to the octagonal tower at the centre: this effect is now best seen in old illustrations, since the southern part of the Observatory garden has been swamped by utilitarian hospital buildings. The two lower floors of the south front, with the central bays canted forward, echo Sir William Chambers' domestic-looking Observatory built for King George III at Richmond in 1768-9, and their basic form, though not their detailing, may have been inherited from Keene.[45] The north side is quite different, its bold semicircular shape echoing the Broad Street facade of Wren's Sheldonian Theatre and perhaps also James Gibbs's Radcliffe Camera, where a semicircular spiral staircase is also concealed behind a curved facade. Any potential heaviness is mitigated by the arrangement of paired Ionic pilasters, niches and Coade stone panels at *piano nobile* level,[46] embellishments which failed to please the hypercritical Edward Tatham, who complained in 1777 that in 'this building, which is large and bulky, we see the most trifling and delicate architecture ... Did [Wyatt] expect to amuse the University of Oxford with his butter-prints and Italian baubles?'[47]

In the design of the top floor, comprising the upper Observatory (Plate 10, p. 17), Wyatt showed himself to be one of the most creative architects of his generation. The Tower of the Winds in Athens, built c.50-40 BC, (Plate 13, p. 25) was described by Vitruvius, the writer of the only architectural treatise to have survived from classical antiquity.[48] But the building itself was little known to westerners until the publication of Julien-David Le Roy's *Les Ruines des Plus Beaux Monuments de la Grèce* in Paris in 1758 and the first volume of the *Antiquities of Athens* by James ('Athenian') Stuart and Nicholas Revett in London in 1762. Originally designed as a horologium or time-keeping device, surmounted by a weathervane, it became after the Ottoman conquest, in Stuart's words, 'a Place of great Devotion in which, at stated times, certain Dervises [sic] perform the circular Mohammedan Dance'.[49] Despite being sunk fifteen feet into the ground and surrounded by houses, its structure and carved decoration remained largely intact, and Stuart and Revett's meticulous drawings allowed it to serve as the inspiration for a garden temple at West Wycombe, Buckinghamshire, of 1759, possibly designed by Revett, and for Stuart's Temples of the Winds at Shugborough, Staffordshire (c.1764-5), and Mount Stewart, Northern Ireland (1782-3).[50] None of these structures are precise copies of the Tower of the Winds, and in the Observatory Wyatt took even greater liberties with the original, inserting large windows and varying the lengths of the eight sides so as to turn the plan into a square with canted corners rather than a true octagon. Nevertheless, for all its lack of archaeological accuracy – never an important aim for Wyatt – the tower makes a statement of the utmost significance for the future of architecture in Europe. The use of a Grecian source, albeit of a late, Hellenistic, type, for a public building was virtually unprecedented in the 1770s, and it must have seemed particularly surprising in a scientific building in Oxford, widely seen as a bastion of clerical obscurantism. The Tower of the Winds was, however, a particularly appropriate model for an observatory. It was designed as a public building, and stood in an important public space. It was embellished externally with sculpture of great beauty and sophistication, there were sundials carved on the stonework outside, and the interior originally housed a water-clock from which movements of the stars could be predicted.[51] So Wyatt's tower not only proclaimed Oxford's conversion to the cause of Grecian architecture; it also made a statement about the building's function.

The external sculpture, not carried out until the 1790s, is one of the few coherent neo-classical programmes of sculptural embellishment in an English public building of its date, and is described in detail in Chapter 2. The Tower of the Winds in Athens has figures representing the classical Winds (north, north east, east, etc.) carved on each of the eight sides below cornice level, each with its name and attributes. The Observatory tower was likewise embellished in 1792-4 with *in situ* carvings of the Winds in Bibury stone by John Bacon (Plate 10, p. 17),[52] creator of the splendidly solid statue of the lawyer Sir William Blackstone in the Codrington Library at All Souls College (1784) and one of the most successful English sculptors of his age. His figures echo the Athenian originals, which had been illustrated by Stuart and Revett, but they do not copy them; and they have something of the linear energy of William Blake's drawings,[53] while at the same time anticipating carvings of the Winds made by Eric Gill and others for Charles Holden's London Transport headquarters at 55 Broadway, London, in 1928-9.[54] Bacon also designed the metal figures of Atlas and Herakles supporting the copper globe at the top of the building, installed in August 1794.[55] The remaining sculptures, over the first-floor windows, are of Coade stone, in the production of which Bacon had been involved since the firm's inception.[56] They consist of a series of rectangular plaques of the signs of the Zodiac by J. C. F. Rossi, the son of an Italian emigrant, dated about 1790 (Plates 15-19, pp. 26-8), and longer panels of Morning, Noon and Evening also by Rossi

(Plates 20-2, p. 29), based on drawings by Robert Smirke, father of the architect of the British Museum (1792).[57] Breaking up the otherwise plain surfaces of the building, these panels further underline its function and meaning, thus adding to its 'decided character'.

The interior of the central block comprised an entrance hall on the ground floor flanked by two smaller rooms, with a staircase mounting up from behind the hall to the lecture room – the 'room for experimental philosophy' demanded by Hornsby in 1768 – and the 'room for occasional observations' in the tower. Nothing was done to fit up these rooms until 1787, when Wyatt was asked to prepare estimates for decorating the lecture room, though two years later Hornsby was complaining of his neglect in not carrying out the work:[58] this was an almost universal vexation for Wyatt's clients. It was completed in 1789, and was followed in 1791 by the lecture room and in 1792-5 by the observatory room.[59] When finally completed, the rooms offered one of the most satisfying 'architectural promenades' (to use Le Corbusier's phrase) in Oxford, demonstrating a progression from darkness to abundant light and, perhaps, from ignorance to enlightenment. The entrance hall (now Green College's common room) was originally entered from the south through a porch modelled directly on the entrances to the Tower of the Winds (Plates 13, p. 25 and 62, p. 168). It is a relatively low, shadowy room surrounded by massive Tuscan columns from which spring strange, quasi-Gothic ribs embellished with roundels, which may be of Coade stone (Plate 11, p. 18).[60] From the far side the staircase mounts to the former lecture room (currently the College dining room), a much lighter room with a delicate Adamesque plaster ceiling similar to that of the hall at Worcester College (1783-4), and arched openings leading into barrel-vaulted bays for storing apparatus (since closed

off) to the north west and north east (Plate 12, p. 18).

The Observatory on the top floor is the most beautiful, though from a practical point of view the least essential, room in the building (Plate 6, p. 14). Wyatt made no attempt to echo the Grecian language of the Tower of the Winds, whose interior was both plain and dark. Instead he chose the model of a Roman-inspired domed rotunda, as in his mausoleum for Lord Yarborough at Brocklesby, Lincolnshire (1786-92).[61] Here, however, the room is flooded with light from tall windows, two of which (on the east and west sides) could be opened from floor level to allow the telescopes to be taken out onto the adjoining roofs. Corinthian columns flank the window openings (in contrast to the heavy and 'primitive' Tuscan columns of the entrance hall), and above them is a gallery with an iron balustrade reached by an iron staircase of complex, somewhat Soaneian, design, for which a Mr Mackell was paid £507 in 1796.[62] The domed ceiling is broken up by delicately embellished 'ribs' recalling Wyatt's hall ceiling at Heveningham Hall, Suffolk (c.1780-4). Wyatt was ordered in 1797 to supply furnishings including a mahogany ladder, a set of steps, six mahogany chairs and a telescope stand for the 'upper room', 24 chairs and a table for the lecture room, and six chairs for the entrance hall, and several of these items survive in the building, though the telescopes shown in Ackermann's engraving of 1814 have long been removed.[63]

The Radcliffe Observatory did not leave any progeny in Oxford, nor indeed anywhere else. Advances in the science and technology of telescopes made quadrants, zenith sectors and tower observatories virtually redundant by the early nineteenth century. The future belonged to lower, domed buildings like those erected at Edinburgh (1818),[64] and Cambridge (1823),[65] housing refracting telescopes of much greater range than the instruments in the Radcliffe Observatory. They were capable of examining the surfaces of the stars and planets, not just their movements. A heliometer for such telescopes was built to the south east of the Observatory in 1848, followed in 1900-3 by another domed structure (since demolished) for another, more powerful, telescope to the south west: meanwhile, in 1874-5 a totally new observatory was built on the southern edge of the University Parks, to the designs of the younger Charles Barry.[66] In a sense the Radcliffe Observatory was always a magnificent anachronism, and in 1935 it was finally abandoned by the Radcliffe Trustees, who moved their observing operations to South Africa.[67] Increasingly encroached upon to the south by the Radcliffe Infirmary, the building was then used for many years by the Nuffield Institute for Medical Research, and in 1960-9 it was refaced under the direction of Marshall Sisson, using Weldon stone in place of the decayed Headington ashlar of lower floors and wings, though the more durable Windrush stone of the tower was allowed to remain.[68] In 1977 it was taken over by Green College, and it has since flourished as a common room, dining room and library for that college's members.

NOTES

1. This chapter is a slightly revised version of an article by the author published in *The Georgian Group Journal* (2000) X: 122-40.
2. Gunther, R. T. (1923) *Early Science in Oxford*. Oxford Historical Society Publications, Oxford. II: 74-5.
3. For the early history of observatories, including those in China and the Islamic world, see Donnelly, M.C. (1973) *A Short History of Observatories*, University of Oregon Books, Eugene, Oregon; and Muller, P. (1996), Observatory. In, Turner, J. (Ed), *The Dictionary of Art*. Macmillan, London. 337-9.
4. Donnelly (1973) 3 *et seq*; Muller (1996), 339-40. The first tower observatory, and the first

institutional observatory in Europe, was the Torre di San Giovanni at the Vatican, erected by Pope Gregory XIII in 1576-9, but this was built before the invention of the telescope.
5. Donnelly (1973) 26.
6. Gunther (1973) 83.
7. Gunther (1973) 85.
8. Guest, I. (1991) *John Radcliffe and his Trust*. The Radcliffe Trust, London. 52, 227-8.
9. Guest (1991) 210-12.
10. The building is discussed in Hussey, C. (1930) The Radcliffe Observatory. *Country Life*. LXVII 674-81; Dale, A. (1956) *James Wyatt*. Basil Blackwell, Oxford; Donnelly (1973) 44-7; and Morton-Gledhill, R. (1988) The Architecture of Astronomy in the British Isles: a General Study. *Visions in Astronomy* XXXII 263-4 and *passim*.
11. Oxford, Bodleian Library (hereafter Bodleian Library), MS d.d. Radcliffe, e.2, ff. 3-9. The relevant part of the letter is transcribed in Gunther (1923) 88-9; and Guest (1991) 228-9.
12. Chapman, A. (2000) Thomas Hornsby and the Radcliffe Observatory. In, Fauvel, J., Flood, R. and Wilson, R. (Eds), *Oxford Figures: 800 Years of the Mathematical Sciences*, Oxford University Press, Oxford. 170-1. There is a full description of the telescopes (undated) in Hornsby's hand in the library of the Royal Astronomical Society (RAS), Supplementary Radcliffe Papers. I am grateful to Julian Munby for this reference, and to the Librarian of the Royal Astronomical Society, Peter Hingley, for allowing me to see the papers.
13. Illustrated in Donnelly (1973) 29. The tower was flanked by lower buildings leading to pavilions.
14. Bodleian Library (1771) MS d.d. Radcliffe, c.51 (Trustees' Minute Book 1752-9), 3 May 1771.
15. Guest (1991) 230.
16. Colvin, H. (1995) *Biographical Dictionary of British Architects 1600-1840*. Yale University Press, New Haven and London. 573-4.
17. Guest (1991) 232; Bodleian Library, MS d.d. Radcliffe, e.2, ff. 10-18; RAS, Supplementary Radcliffe Papers.
18. Bodleian Library, MS d.d. Radcliffe c. 51; *Jackson's Oxford Journal*. 17 June 1772.

19. C[okayne], G. E. (1926) *The Complete Peerage.* London.VI: 214.
20. Bodleian Library, MS d.d. Radcliffe, c.51 (20 March 1773).
21. Bodleian Library, MS d.d. Radcliffe, c.51 (24 February 1776); Bodleian Library, MS d.d. Radcliffe, c.58.
22. Dale (1956) 3-4.The other Trustees present at the meeting in March 1773 were Lord North, Sir William Drake of Shardeloes, Buckinghamshire, and Sir William Dolben of Finedon Hall, Northants.The minutes record that they were shown the new elevation because of an order from Lord Lichfield, but it is not certain whether this was the recently deceased Third Earl or his successor.
23. These works are discussed in Tyack, G. (1998) *Oxford: an Architectural Guide.* Oxford University Press, Oxford/New York. 173-8.
24. Tatham, E. (1773) *Oxonia Explicata et Ornata.* Oxford. 23.
25. Colvin (1995) 1111.
26. Colvin (1995) 746.
27. Wyatt's Oxford work is discussed in Tyack (1998) 183-91.
28. But see note 30 below.
29. Guest (1991) 241.
30. There is a photograph of the stable block in its original condition in the Bodleian Library (Plate 37, p. 60), MS d.d. Radcliffe, d.43, f. 8. The Professor's house is now used by the college for offices and student accommodation.
31. Bodleian Library, MS d.d. Radcliffe, e.2, f. 44.
32. Bird's letters about the supply and delivery of the instruments is preserved in RAS, Supplementary Radcliffe Papers.
33. Oxford, Corpus Christi College, MS CCC 443 (X). The drawing is reproduced in Harrison, C. (Ed.) (1998) *John Malchair of Oxford,* Ashmolean Museum, Oxford. 76.
34. Guest (1991) 241-2; Bodleian Library, MS d.d. Radcliffe, d.43, f. 33.
35. National Maritime Museum, Greenwich, transcript of diary of Thomas Bugge (hereafter Bugge Diary) in the Royal Library, Copenhagen, 6 October 1777. I am grateful to Professor G. L'Estrange Turner for this reference.
36. Gunther (1923) 90.
37. The cornice moulding may also be of Coade stone (Alison Kelly (1990) *Mrs Coade's Stone,* Upton-on-Severn, 164). The *paterae* featured in the Coade catalogue for 1784 (Kelly, 1990, 167).
38. Bugge Diary, 6 Oct 1777. Bugge clearly envisaged a two- and not a three-storey tower, with the ground floor used as a reading room and the telescopes in the room upstairs. His sketch, possibly based on Keene's lost design, shows a circular domed building flanked by the two lower wings.
39. Bodleian Library MS d.d. Radcliffe c.51 (24 February 1776); MS d.d. Radcliffe, e.2, f. 44.
40. Bodleian Library MS d.d. Radcliffe, c.51 (15 May 1776).
41. Bodleian Library, MS Top. Oxon., b.222, f. 24; Bodleian Library MS d.d. Radcliffe, c.51 (27 November 1777).
42. Bodleian Library, MS d.d. Radcliffe, e. 2, f. 44.
43. Bodleian Library MS d.d. Radcliffe, c.51 (15 May 1776, 20 March 1780); MS d.d. Radcliffe, c.52 (18 May 1799).
44. Quoted in Donnelly (1973) 29.
45. Donnelly (1973) 39-43.
46. The Ionic capitals are also of Coade stone.
47. Tatham, E. (1777) *Oxonia Explicata et Ornata,* 2nd edition. Oxford. 36-7.
48. Smith, T.G. (2003), *Vitruvius on Architecture,* The Monacelli Press, New York, 78; Robertson, D. S. (1969) *Greek and Roman Architecture.* Cambridge University Press, Cambridge. 338-9.
49. Stuart, J. and Revett, N. (1762) *Antiquities of Athens.* London (4 Volumes) I: 14.
50. Pevsner, N. and Williamson, E. (1994) *The Buildings of England: Buckinghamshire,* Yale University Press, London. 734.
51. I owe this point to the fascinating exhibition on *The Story of Time* held at the Queen's House, Greenwich from 1 December 1999 to 24 September 2000.A picture of a water clock was included in Barbaro's edition of Vitruvius (1556).
52. Bodleian Library, MS d.d. Radcliffe, e.2, f. 45.
53. This point was made by Esdaile, K. (1930) The Radcliffe Observatory. *Journal of the Royal Society of Arts,* LXXVIII: 755-9.
54. Collins, J. (1992) *Eric Gill: Sculpture.* Barbican Art Gallery, London. 108-9.

55. Guest (1991) 245; Bodleian Library, MS d.d. Radcliffe, e.2, f. 45. There was a payment of £70 10s for the globe on 17 May 1794 to 'Horsley and Catherwood' (Bodleian Library, MS d.d. Radcliffe c. 52), the latter presumably Thomas Catherwood who supplied a brass fireplace for the Library at Stowe, Buckinghamshire in 1805 (Bevington, M. (1990) *Stowe Guide*. 48). I am grateful to Richard Hewlings for this reference.

56. Gunnis, R. (1968) *Dictionary of British Sculptors 1660-1851.* Abbey Library, London. 24.

57. Bodleian Library, MS d.d. Radcliffe, e.2, f. 47. For Rossi, see Gunnis (1968) 326-8.

58. Bodleian Library MS d.d. Radcliffe, c. 51. (15 May 1787, 26 May and 9 June 1789)

59. Bodleian Library MS d.d. Radcliffe, c. 52 (27 May 1791); MS d.d. Radcliffe, e.2, f. 45 (14 June 1792).

60. Dale (1956) 83.

61. Pevsner, N., Harris, J. and Antram, N. (1989) *The Buildings of England: Lincolnshire.* Yale University Press, London. 190-1

62. Bodleian Library (7 May 1796) MS d.d. Radcliffe, c.52. Mackell was presumably either John Mackell, who worked at Somerset House, London, in 1776-95, or James Mackell, who worked for Soane at No. 33, St James's Square, London, between 1817 and 1823, and at the Law Courts in 1820-25 (*History of the King's Works*, V, 467; *Survey of London*, XXIX, 208). I am grateful to Richard Hewlings for these references.

63. Bodleian Library MS d.d. Radcliffe, c.52 (6 May 1797); Ackermann, R. (1814) *History of the University of Oxford*, London. II: 240-1.

64. Youngson, A. J. (1966) *The Making of Classical Edinburgh.* Edinburgh University Press, Edinburgh. 159.

65. For the Cambridge Observatory, see Willis, R. and Clark, J. (1886) *The Architectural History of the University of Cambridge*, Cambridge University Press, Cambridge. III: 190-8. The first observatory in Cambridge was built on the gate tower of Trinity College in 1706.

66. For the history of the buildings in the nineteenth and twentieth centuries, see Guest (1991) 265, 291-3; Chapman, in Fauvel, Flood and Wilson (1999) 181-4.

67. Guest (1991) 465-6.

68. Oakeshott, W. F. (ed.) (1975) *Oxford Stone Restored.* Oxford Historic Buildings Fund, Oxford. 34-5.

Plate 1. 'Near the Observatory', watercolour by J. B. Malchair, 1774, looking northwards on the Woodstock Road with the Royal Oak inn on the right and the Observatory's boundary wall on the left (*by permission of the President and Fellows of Corpus Christi College, Oxford*)

Plate 2. 'The beginning of the Observatory, Oxford', watercolour by J. B. Malchair, 1774. The gravel drive to the completed Observer's House (*by permission of the President and Fellows of Corpus Christi College, Oxford*)

Plate 3. The Observatory under construction from the north east,
watercolour by J. B. Malchair, 1777 (*Green College, Oxford*)

Plate 4. 'The Observatory from the south east' from R. Ackermann,
A History of the University of Oxford, 1814 (*Green College, Oxford*)

Plate 5. 'View of Oxford, from the Gallery of the Observatory', also from R. Ackermann,
A History of the University of Oxford, 1814 (*Green College, Oxford*)

Plate 6. 'The interior of the tower' showing the portable Dollond refractors and the Herschel reflector, from R. Ackermann, *A History of the University of Oxford*, 1814 (*Green College, Oxford*)

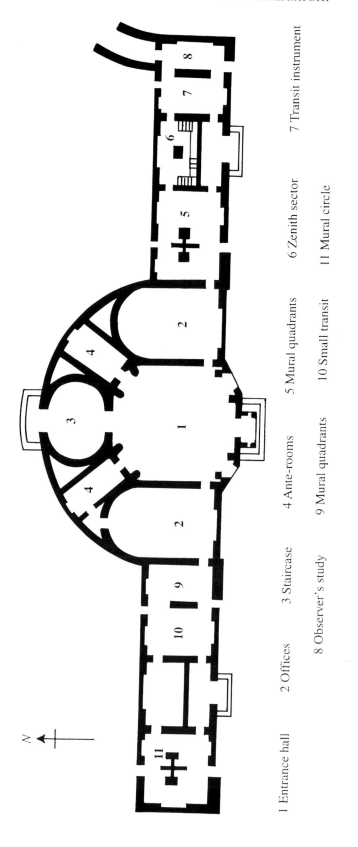

Plate 7. Plan of the central block showing the original uses of the rooms (*Wilbur Wright*)

1 Entrance hall   2 Offices   3 Staircase   4 Ante-rooms   5 Mural quadrants   6 Zenith sector   7 Transit instrument

8 Observer's study   9 Mural quadrants   10 Small transit   11 Mural circle

Plate 8. Interior of the east wing showing Bird's south quadrant and the viewing slots from the inside (*The Bodleian Library, Oxford, courtesy The Radcliffe Trust*)

Plate 9. The east wing from the south. The light vertical line of stones marks the slots for the meridian instruments (*Geoffrey Tyack*)

Plate 10. The tower from the north west (*Geoffrey Tyack*)

Plate 11. The entrance hall, c.1930 (*The Bodleian Library, Oxford, courtesy The Radcliffe Trust*)

Plate 12. The former lecture room, c.1930 (*The Bodleian Library, Oxford, courtesy The Radcliffe Trust*)

Chapter 2

Allegorical Figures on the Radcliffe Observatory

Michael Popkin

As recorded in Chapter 1, the building of the Radcliffe Observatory was begun in 1772 to the design of Henry Keene (died 1776), it was completed to a different design by James Wyatt (1746-1813). The design of the eight-sided tower is Wyatt's and is based on the much smaller octagonal Tower of the Winds in Athens, an illustration of which had appeared in Stuart and Revett's *Antiquities of Athens* published in 1762[1] (Plates 13, p. 25). The Tower in Athens, only 25½ feet in diameter, was built in the first century BC as a horologium (clock-tower) with a water-clock in a turret on the tower, sundials on the sides, a weather-vane on the top and a personified Wind on each face of the octagon.

The exterior of the Radcliffe Observatory is decorated with allegorical figures. On the roof is a globe supported by two figures (by John Bacon). Round the top of the building are eight personified Winds (also by John Bacon) and below are three panels representing Morning, Noon and Evening (by Robert Smirke). The Winds are in Windrush stone (from Bibury);[2] the Signs of the Zodiac and the three panels are in Coade stone,[3] an artificial stone manufactured between 1770 and the 1830s by a process whose secret was lost for over 150 years until its recent rediscovery.

The Globe and its supporting figures

In Plate III of *Antiquities of Athens* Stuart and Revett showed the Tower of the Winds as being topped with a weather-vane in the form of the figure of Triton, which revolved with the wind. The figure was not, in fact, present on the Tower in the eighteenth century, and was added by Stuart and Revett to their drawing on the strength of a description given by the Roman architect, Vitruvius, in the first century BC.

Instead of Triton, the Radcliffe Observatory has a globe supported by the figures of Atlas and Herakles. The figures are variously reported to be made of 'cast iron' (Hussey[4] and Gray[5]), of 'lead' (Pevsner[6]) and of 'bronze' (Gunnis[7]). The most acceptable authority is Peter Inskip, the architect for the recent conservation work, who describes them as lead. The globe is described as 'copper' by Hussey and as 'copper-sheathed' by Pevsner. According to Inskip (see Chapter 8) the globe may originally have been of lead and was replaced in the 1970s in copper.

In Greek mythology, Atlas was condemned to support the heavens on his head and hands as a punishment for taking part in a revolt against Zeus.[8] He was later changed into the range of mountains that bears his name. He is usually depicted supporting the globe on his own but here he is joined by that other strong man of Greek myth, Herakles (Latin 'Hercules').

The names of Atlas and Herakles are linked in the myth of the Golden Apples in the Garden of Hesperides, a garden on the slopes of Mount Atlas.[9] Herakles who, as the eleventh of his Twelve Labours, had to slay a serpent in order to get the apples, persuaded Atlas to pick up the apples while he himself temporarily took over the burden of supporting the world. Atlas is supposed to have taught Herakles about astronomy, and the pair of them became recognized as an allegory of astronomy. It is appropriate therefore that they should preside over the Radcliffe Observatory.

The eight personified Winds

In antiquity, the winds were regarded as deities, usually four in number (Boreas, Notos, Zephyros and Euros) whose master, Aeolus, kept them locked up in a cave.[10] When they escaped or were let out, the winds blew.

On the Tower of the Winds in Athens, eight winds are depicted, one on each face of the octagon (Plate 13, p. 25) and it is Stuart and Revett's illustrations of these that the sculptor John Bacon[11] used as the basis for his designs of the flying figures on the Radcliffe Observatory (Plate 15, p. 26). Each of the flying figures on the Observatory is on the appropriate face of the octagon, e.g. Boreas, the north wind, is on the north face. The figures are all male, each one being accompanied by its name in Greek capitals.[12]

The Signs of the Zodiac

The twelve Signs of the Zodiac did not form part of the decoration of the original Tower of the Winds in Athens. For the Radcliffe Observatory, the sculptor J. C. F. Rossi (1762-1839)[13] based his designs not on Stuart and Revett but on illustrations contained in Spence's *Polymetis,* first published in 1747.[14] Spence, in turn, had obtained his illustrations of the zodiac from the Farnese Globe, a

---

The eight personified winds of antiquity

Boreas, the cold north wind (from which the name *Aurora borealis* derives) who wears warm clothes and holds a conch, to indicate the howling noise of the cold north wind.

Notos, the south wind, the *sirocco* of modern Italy ('Auster' in Latin and from which the words Australia and Australasia are derived) is a blustery, wet wind, as indicated by the folds of the mantle and by the pitcher from which water is gushing.

Zephyros, the gentle west wind, which translates directly into 'zephyr' is depicted as a naked youth carrying flowers in the folds of his mantle, indicative of the mild, light westerly breeze.

Euros, the south-east wind, was warm and rain-bringing. The folds of his garment suggest heavy clouds.

Kaikias, the north-east wind, has wet hair and holds a shield-shaped basin from which he tips hailstones.

Skiron, the north-west wind, is an old man with an oven-jar, indicating that the dry north-west wind dries up vegetation.

Apeliotes, the east wind, is a youth with light footwear holding a harvest of fruit, grain and honey in the folds of his mantle. Wind from the east brought mild weather and gentle rain.

Lips, the south-west wind, blew straight into the harbour of Piraeus, making homecoming easy but preventing ships from sailing out. A young man is shown holding a ship's stern-post, thus preventing the ship from sailing.

celestial globe marked with over forty constellations, that has survived from Roman times (Plate 14, p. 25).

The Farnese Globe was the model for the Globe at the apex of the Observatory, but here it is supported by the figures of Atlas and Herakles, rather than Triton, for aesthetic and structural balance and for the sake of public modesty (See Chapter 8). The name 'Farnese' derives from the Farnese Palace in Rome, where Spence reported its presence in the eighteenth century. The globe is now in the Museo Nationale in Naples.[15] There seems to be no doubt of its authenticity, even though the kneeling figure of Atlas which supports it is a Renaissance copy. Celestial globes are known to have existed both in ancient Greece and in Rome, but it seems that the Farnese Globe is the only one to have survived. It is thought to be a Roman copy of a Greek original.[16] A comparison between Spence's illustrations from the Farnese Globe and the figures on the Radcliffe Observatory leaves no doubt that Rossi's designs are very similar to – some even identical with – the original.

It has long been recognized that the names given by both Greeks and Romans to the twelve signs of the zodiac derive from Greek mythology. Some of the myths were brought to light in an English translation by Edward Sherburne[17] of the Latin author Manilius, published in 1675, and others were identified in the following century by Spence,[18] who quotes references to other Latin authors (including Virgil and Ovid), in which myths are attached to the signs. Further explanations of the mythological origins of the signs have been made since the eighteenth century. The following list is taken, as far as possible, from Sherburne and Spence; the associated illustrations show some of the figures after restoration in 2004 (Plates 15-19, pp. 26-8).

Aries (Ram). The ram whose golden fleece was recovered by Jason, leader of the Argonauts (Spence).

Taurus (Bull). The bull whose form Zeus (Jupiter) assumed when he abducted Europa (Spence, quoting Virgil).

Gemini (Twins). Castor and Polydeuces (Pollux), the twin heroes (Castor as a tamer of horses and Polydeuces as a boxer) known as the Dioscuri, who sailed with Jason in quest of the golden fleece (Spence, quoting Ovid).

Cancer (Crab). The crab that pinched Herakles while he was performing the second of his Twelve Labours by fighting with the Lernaean hydra.[19]

Leo (Lion). The Nemean lion slain by Herakles as the first of his Twelve Labours (Spence, quoting Manilius). The lion's skin became the attribute by which Herakles is identified in Greek statuary.

Virgo (Virgin). Astraea, who stood for justice and innocence, and who reluctantly left the earth for the heavens when sin began to prevail (Spence, quoting Avienus, Hall and Brewer[20] concur).

Libra (Scales). Anyone who takes the trouble to count the Zodiac panels on the Radcliffe Observatory will be struck by the fact that there are only eleven of them. The reason for this is that two of the signs (Libra and Scorpio) are combined on one panel. (Plate 17, p. 28) The Scales being held up in the claws of the Scorpion.[21] The early Greeks recognized only eleven signs of the Zodiac, and referred to what we now call Libra as 'the claws of the scorpion'. In about the third century BC, they gave the sign the separate name of 'zygon' (a yoke), which the Romans interpreted as 'libra' (scales).[22] The Latin word 'libra' (from which we get the abbreviation lb) referred to the basic unit of weight as well as to the weighing-scales. According to Spence,[23] the name Libra was given to the zodiacal sign only after the death of the Emperor Augustus (AD 14) as a compliment to him for 'holding a balance in the affairs of the world'. It has also been pointed out that Libra occurs at the time of the autumnal equinox when day and night are in equal balance.[24]

As will be seen in the illustration, Rossi

followed Spence's faithful reproduction from the Farnese Globe by modelling both the signs in a single panel and depicting the Scales in the claws of the Scorpion.

Sherburne states that 'there is no distinct Fable for this Sign' (Libra). The only myth that has been suggested is that of Astraea (*vide* Virgo) as goddess of justice, presumably on the grounds that one of the attributes of Justice is a pair of scales.

Scorpio (Scorpion). Neither Sherburne nor Spence offer an explanation. Two more recent theories[25] are: (i) the scorpion that stung Orion to death. (In support of this theory is the fact that Orion always gets out of the way by setting just as Scorpio rises!); or (ii) the scorpion that caused the horses of the sun to bolt when they were being driven for a day by the inexperienced Phaeton.

Sagittarius (Archer) called Arcitenens by Spence. Either, a satyr who afflicted Zeus in his battle against rebel giants,[26] or, Chiron, a centaur, who was accidentally pierced by a poisoned arrow shot by Herakles during the fourth of his Twelve Labours.[27] A mystery surrounds the hoop-like wreath carried by Sagittarius. Spence suggests that it is not part of Sagittarius but a separate constellation, but he is at a loss to name the constellation.[28]

Capricornus (Sea-goat: a goat with a fish-tail). Spence claimed that such a monster could only be 'some sort of hieroglyphical language',[29] but a subsequent theory holds that Pan, in order to escape the monster Typhon, jumped into the water just as he was changing into an animal shape. The half above the water assumed the shape of a goat while the lower half became a fish.[30]

Aquarius (Water-carrier). All sources agree that this is Ganymede, cup-bearer to Zeus.

Pisces (Fish). Various explanations include: (i) the river from which Aquarius drew water;[31] (ii) the fish who carried Aphrodite and Eros to safety when they jumped into a river to escape the monster Typhon (*vide* Capricornus);[32] or (iii) when fleeing from Typhon, the gods

disguised themselves as animals. Aphrodite and Eros succeeded in changing themselves into fish, but Pan (*vide* Capricornus) was just too late.[33]

Two mnemonics might assist those who find difficulty in remembering the order of the Signs:[34]

Our vernal signs the Ram begins,
Then comes the Bull, in May the Twins;
The Crab in June, next Leo shines
And Virgo ends the northern signs.
The Balance brings autumnal fruits,
The Scorpion stings, the Archer shoots;
December's Goat brings wintry blast,
Aquarius rain, the Fish comes last.
★★★
The Ram, the Bull, the Heavenly Twins
And next the Crab and Lion shines,
The Virgin and the Scales.
The Scorpion, Archer and Sea-Goat,
The Man that bears the water-pot
And Fish with glittering tails.

The Morning, Noon and Evening panels

Set between the last four zodiacal signs on the north face of the Observatory are three rectangular panels, representing Morning, Noon and Evening, with figures in relief in Coade stone (Plates 20-2, p. 29). These were modelled by Robert Smirke (1752-1825), father of the more illustrious Sir Robert Smirke (1781-1867)[35] who designed the British Museum[36]. The panels do not appear on the Tower of the Winds in Athens. There are no detailed records from the Coade factory for the period when the Observatory was being built, and no contemporary description of the figures has been traced.[36] Identification of the figures is therefore made here purely on icono-graphical evidence.

The Morning panel (on the east face) has three figures. Prominent in the centre is a female figure carrying a pitcher in her right hand and a lamp, lit by a star, in her left hand. These attributes identify her as Eos (Latin

'Aurora') or Dawn, the pitcher being a container for morning dew[38] which she scatters, and the star representing the Morning Star (the planet Venus) characterized by Phosphoros.[39] Following behind the figure of Eos is a chariot drawn by four horses (a 'quadriga') rising out of the clouds, driven by Helios (the Sun), brother of Eos. On the right of the panel is a recumbent female figure (left forearm missing) who wears a castellated crown and who is looking at the Morning Star. The turreted crown identifies her as Cybele, the Phrygian earth-mother, who here personifies the Earth, waiting to be refreshed by the dew.[40]

The central panel, on the north face, has the single figures of Helios standing in his four-horse chariot at the noon-tide zenith of his journey across the sky.

The panel on the west face represents Evening or, perhaps more accurately, The Approach of Night. The figure in the two-horse chariot is identifiable as Nyx (Night) by the veil over her head and the stars which surround her.[41] She is looking backwards at another female figures who carries a bow and who has a small crescent moon on her brow. These attributes identify her as Artemis (the Roman goddess Diana), goddess of the moon.[42] As Nyx and Artemis set off together on their journey, they pass a third figure (left forearm missing) who sits in a posture of weariness and by whose side is a spade. This figure may be intended to represent Sleep; however, the spade is often used in Renaissance art as an attribute of Work[43] and may here be indicative of work ceasing in the evening.

It is very fitting in the Oxford environment that a building with such strong and precise classical links should be used for the perennial tasks of education and inquiry. Despite the dramatic changes of use from the originally intended astronomical observation through medical research to graduate education and student life, the classical origins have been upheld. The several adornments on the Observatory building, reflecting personifications of mythical figures that had great importance for previous civilizations, will continue to enlighten and inspire modern generations. The sympathetic restoration at the start of the third millennium is enhancing the visibility of the building and its attraction to academics, historians and the public at large.

NOTES

1. Stuart, J. and Revett, N. (1762) Of the Octagon Tower of Andronicus Cyrrheotes. In *Antiquities of Athens.* London (4 Volumes) Vol. I, Ch. III.
2. Gray, A. S. (1958) The Radcliffe Observatory. *Oxford Medical School Gazette.* 10: 69.
3. The words 'COADE, LONDON' appear on the Evening panel, and the word 'COADE' with the date '1796' is still legible on the zodiac panel of Leo. The words are more faintly discernible on some of the other zodiac panels.
4. Hussey (1930).
5. Gray (1958) 50.
6. Pevsner, *op. cit.,* 272. Sherwood, J. and Pevsner, N. (1974) *The Buildings of England: Oxfordshire.* Penguin, Harmondsworth. 272.
7. Gunnis, R. (1968) *Dictionary of British Sculptors 1660-1851.* Abbey Library, London. 26.
8. Hall, J. (1984) *Dictionary of Subjects and Symbols in Art.* Revised Edition. John Murray, London. 35.
9. Hall (1984) 150.
10. Hall (1984) 341.
11. John Bacon (1740-99) was a prolific sculptor whose work can be seen all over the country. Probably the finest specimen of his work in Oxford is the statue of Sir William Blackstone in the Codrington Library of All Souls. Christ Church also has good examples. London has outdoor statuary as well as monuments in Westminster Abbey (notably his monument to William Pitt) and in St Paul's Cathedral (especially his statues of Dr Samuel Johnson and of John Howard, the prison reformer). Bacon's son, John Bacon, 'The Younger' (1777-1859) was also a sculptor (*vide* Gunnis (1953) 26-28).

12. The attributions of the Winds are taken from: Baumeister, A. (1889) *Denkmaler des klassischen Altertums*, Article on Wind-towers.

13. Sculptures by J. C. F. Rossi are to be found on public buildings and in churches throughout England, including some in St Paul's Cathedral. He also sculpted the bust of James Wyatt (architect of the Observatory) now in the National Portrait Gallery (NPG 344) (*vide* Gunnis (1953) 328-9, and Yung, K. K. (1981) *National Portrait Gallery Complete Illustrated Catalogue*. London).

14. Spence, J. (1755) *Polymetis*. London. Second edition. Plate XXIV.

15. Muris, O. and Saarman, G. (1961) *Der Globus im Wandel der Zeiten*. Columbus Verlag Paul Oestergaard KG.

16. Savage-Smith, E. (1985) *Islamicate Celestial Globes*. Smithsonian Institute Press, Washington DC. 11.

17. Sherburne, E. (1675). *The Sphere of M. Manilius made an English Poem*. London.

18. Spence (1755).

19. *The New Encyclopaedia Britannica* (1974) 15th edition. 'Cancer'.

20. Hall (1984); *Brewer's Dictionary of Phrase and Fable* (1984) Centenary Edition.

21. *The New Encyclopaedia Britannica* (1974) 'Libra'.

22. *The New Encyclopaedia Britannica* (1974) 'Scorpio'.

23. Spence (1755) 69.

24. *Brewer's Dictionary of Phrase and Fable* (1984) Centenary Edition. 640.

25. Both from *The New Encyclopaedia Britannica* (1974) 'Scorpio'.

26. Spence (1755) 169.

27. *The New Encyclopaedia Britannica* (1974) 'Sagittarius'.

28. Spence (1755) 176.

29. Spence (1755) 169.

30. *The New Encyclopaedia Britannica* (1974) 'Capricornus'.

31. Spence (1755) quoting Ovid.

32. *The New Encyclopaedia Britannica* (1974) 'Pisces'

33. *Pears Encyclopaedia* (1958-59) Greek myths and legends: Typhon.

34. From *A Dictionary of Mnemonics* (1972) Eyre Methuen, London. 9.

35. *Chambers Biographical Dictionary* (1984) Revised Edition. 1238.

36. Francis, Sir F. (Ed.) (1971) *Treasures of the British Museum*. Thames and Hudson.

37. Alison Kelly, Private communication.

38. Ripa, C. (1645) *Iconologia*, Venice. 125-6.

39. Spence (1755) Dialogue XII: Planets, Times and Seasons.

40. Hall (1984) 26, 36, 89 and 128.

41. de Montfaucon, B. (1721) *Antiquity Explained*. London. I: 227 ff.

42. Hall (1984) 51 and 196.

43. The Warburg Institute, London. Private communication.

Plate 13. The Tower of the Winds, Athens, from J. Stuart and N. Revett, *The Antiquities of Athens*, 1762–1830

Plate 14. The Farnese Globe (*The Naples Museum*)

Plate 15. The Tower of the Winds with Zephyros and Aries

Plate 16. Leo

Plate 17. Libra and Scorpio

Plate 18. Aquarius

Plate 19. Pisces

Plate 20. The Coade stone plaque of 'Morning'

Plate 21. The Coade stone plaque of 'Noon'

Plate 22. The Coade stone plaque of 'Evening'

Chapter 3

A History of the Gardens and Grounds of the Radcliffe Observatory

Michael Pirie

Although the gardens of the Radcliffe Observatory were completely incidental to its main function (just as they are to Green College's), the fact that advances in astronomy have rendered the work of the Radcliffe Observers largely obsolete allows us to consider other histories of the institution. I hope in this chapter to advance the significance of the history of its gardens.

Placed in a local context, the Observatory is of interest to garden history because it represents a rare case of a substantial garden layout being created from scratch in Oxford during the late eighteenth century through to the early nineteenth. It therefore grants us an insight into the way that the precepts of the landscape movement were assimilated into a new garden.

In relation to the University it occupies a mid-point in the large gap between the founding of Worcester College (1714) and Keble College (1870), and while most college gardens underwent considerable change at the time of the nascent Observatory, they did so by adaptation rather than creation. Furthermore, the Observatory gave accommodation merely to an astronomer and very few employees, so that in terms of buildings and domestic arrangements it had more in common with a country house than a collegiate institution.

The distinct compartments into which the grounds were separated – pasture, park, stable yard, kitchen and private garden – combined to form a distinct economic unit that was designed, at least initially, to be self-sufficient. From the mid-nineteenth century the gardens exhibited the eclectic floral interests of the Victorians, paralleling the development of north Oxford as a residential suburb.

The integrity of the grounds began to be eroded with the expansion of the hospital on its margins towards the end of the nineteenth century, and the erosion continued with the effects of the First World War, but since space was the indispensable requirement of an observatory, around as well as above it, the extent, if not the form of the grounds was bound to endure for as long as the institution itself. The main threat to their unity, and indeed to their very existence, therefore, came with the proposals associated with the relocation of the Observatory. That the possibility of its demolition should have been entertained, if only briefly, gives us an insight into the vagaries of periodic decision making which just might have seen a housing development substituted for a place of medical research (and ultimately Green College).

If the grounds to the south and west of the Observatory were largely surrendered to the expansion of the hospital during the 1930s, and the kitchen garden later adapted to provide sporting facilities for Osler House, the retreat stopped at the boundary of the Observer's private garden. So despite the loss of the vast majority of the original grounds of the Radcliffe Observatory, some sense of the importance of what was left was in evidence right up to the time of the founding of Green College.

The sections of this chapter are arranged in the sequence of Radcliffe Observers for a number of reasons, quite apart from chronology. In the absence of a direct voice from the gardeners themselves, much of the available information comes from statements that were articulated by those who oversaw the establishment and often took an interest in its appearance. Moreover, the fact that appointments were almost invariably held until death made the arrival of each new Observer represent something of a watershed in the way that the Observatory was to proceed, for his first task was to report on the state of the institution and to recommend alterations or improvements.

Early years 1769–1810. Thomas Hornsby and the drawings of J. B. Malchair

We are used to the Radcliffe Observatory being surrounded. Whether we consider the building in its immediate proximity to others, or subsumed within the larger area of north Oxford, we do not naturally think of it as being on the edge of the city. In the first instance, therefore, I want to recreate the time and place at which the Observatory came into existence, on the margin between the city and the country.

The choice of site for the building resulted from negotiations by its prime mover, Professor Thomas Hornsby, with a number of interested parties. The Trustees of Dr John Radcliffe's estate had agreed in principle in 1769 to fund an observatory, once they had finished paying for the Infirmary. Thomas Hornsby's friend, the noble George, Fourth Duke of Marlborough, being both a keen amateur astronomer and a prominent leaseholder in St Giles Parish, was prepared to donate the land on which to build one. St John's College owned the parochial estate, whose gravelly subsoil was indispensable to structural stability.[1] So if the hospital had been built on the edge of Oxford in order to be apart from the general population, it was with an equal but different need for isolation – the clarity of the night sky – that the Observatory came to be erected next door.

Evidently with a knowledge of the ulterior motive in the agreement, St John's College leased to the Duke in 1769 a plot of land comprising 9 acres 1 rod and 3 perches, known as 'the Garden Piece'.[2] The plot had already appeared incidentally in an early etching by John Baptist Malchair, band leader at the Music Room in Holywell and drawing master, in which capacity he figures prominently in the pictorial record of the early years of the Observatory and its grounds. 'North View' (Plate 23, p. 52), published as one of a series of 12 etchings in 1763,[3] shows 'the Garden Piece' in the foreground, with the pristine north façade of the Infirmary standing out against University buildings silhouetted behind. To what extent the land was cultivated so as to merit its name is unclear, but market gardens flourished around the city at this time.[4]

The approval by the University in 1771 for building the Observatory, the appointment of Henry Keene as architect in 1772 and his later replacement by James Wyatt are covered in detail by Geoffrey Tyack in Chapter 1. I want just to make a few remarks about the disposition of the buildings on the site, since it partly determines how the ground was to be divided and landscaped.

In the first place, it was necessary for the Observatory to be set well back from the road. This was in order not only to be clear of interference from anything on its boundaries, particularly the Infirmary, but also because it had to be aligned on a north/south axis. For the most accurate readings to be taken from the meridian instruments placed within the building there needed to be a fixed mark at some distance due south. The only clear line of sight was to be obtained in the direction of Worcester College, where Keene was also working, and where a suitable wall was found on which to place the mark, some 682 yards distant.[5] So, although the instruments might be used to survey the sky to the north as well, it was the greater significance of the southern sky that determined the principal façade of the building and the emphasis to be placed on its grounds on that side.

As the Observatory itself turned away from the line of the main road to face south, the role of presenting a face to the world fell to the Observer's House whose front pointed south-east in the direction of the main entrance to the institution – its closest access to the city on the 'Road to Woodstock'.[6] The ingenious use of a corridor to link the two structures, along with a curtain wall that joined the Observer's House to the stables, not only unified the architectural elements in the chain but also completely separated different parts of the grounds according to their function.

Riding north from St Giles the road widened, then as now, as it approached the Royal Oak inn – a scene that was captured by Malchair in October 1774, in his drawing 'Near the Observatory'[7] (Plate 1, p. 11). Beyond the inn, open country shows up ahead, and a footpath to the left runs alongside the Infirmary and Observatory wall. The principal entrance is marked by round-topped gate piers (now hospital Gate 5), while access to the stable yard is between similar piers further up the road.

The line of the drive within the precincts of the Observatory was determined initially as much for utilitarian as for aesthetic

reasons, as is implicit in Malchair's drawing 'The beginning of the Observatory, Oxford',[8] also made in October 1774 (Plate 2, p. 11). The supply of stone needed to follow the most direct route to the buildings, and the construction of a drive merely entailed the stripping away of the topsoil in order to expose the gravel beneath. The fact that it was curved rather than straight was a typical period detail, for as William Marshall noted: 'A road of necessity ought to be straighter than one of mere conveniency…but, even in this, the direct line may be dispensed with'.[9]

By the beginning of 1776 the Observer's House (complete with occupant) and the Observatory (which had still not yet risen above ground floor level) had cost close to the original estimate of £6-7,000[10] for the entire building. In May, the Radcliffe Trustees felt obliged to restrict funding to £1,000 a year, in order to match expenditure more closely to the income from Dr Radcliffe's estate, but not before deciding at the same meeting 'to enclose the whole premises with a wall'.[11] This made secure the boundary to the north and west. The hospital wall already served as its southern boundary and by the time of the Trustees' decision, the opportunity had been taken to plant the grounds on that side. An entry in the accounts for February 1776 recorded the payment of £52.9s.0d. to 'Mrs Eliza Tagg, nurserywoman'[12] of Paradise Gardens, for the first substantial quantity of trees and shrubs, duly being planted during the dormant season.

By reference to another of Malchair's drawings (Plate 24, p. 52) we have an idea of what this planting looked like at the end of its first season of growth. 'From the Observatory, December 28th 1776'[13] looks south-east from the Observer's House towards the main entrance, with the Royal Oak appearing over the wall. The initial impact of the young nursery stock is appropriately modest.

The explanation for the frequency with which Malchair drew the Observatory lay in his close acquaintance with Thomas Hornsby and family. He taught drawing to Hornsby's daughter Anne, and her vignette appeared on the reverse of 'The Infirmary at Oxford, from Professor Hornsby's house, January 9th 1778' (Plate 25, p. 53).[14] Drawn from a similar angle to 'North View', the family members are seen walking west along the drive beside the hospital wall towards a clump of trees and shrubs that have quite clearly been planted with a view to obscuring the hospital buildings on the other side.[15]

If members of Hornsby's family took drawing lessons from Malchair, it appears that he himself picked up something from the astronomer,[16] and it may have been to celebrate the winter solstice that he recorded 'The place of the sun's setting as seen from Professor Hornsby's dining parlour at the Observatory, December 20th 1784'[17] (Plate 27, p. 54). (See Appendix 1 for a list of drawings by Malchair relating to the Observatory.)

This drawing represents another example of Malchair's interest in landscape and topography and grants us a view away from the Observatory in contrast to the many familiar images looking towards it. Clearly shown are the sparsely furnished grounds and the completely unfamiliar expanse of open country to Hinksey Hill, confirming that the Observatory, as *The Universal British Directory* of 1798 put it, 'commands a very extensive horizon, and is scarcely in any wise liable to be incommoded by the smoke of the town'.[18] The Equatorial sector house, containing the only instrument that required a view of the whole sky, stood apart from the Observatory in the first 'garden' building, designed after the Temple of Romulus in the Roman forum (and demolished in the 1920s).[19]

The Radcliffe Trustees' primary concern throughout all this time was the completion of the building. Thomas Hornsby, on the other hand, who had lived in the Observer's House since November 1773, and was used to observing and teaching amidst a building site, had both to run the institution and ensure the maintenance of the site. This latter responsibility the Trustees acknowledged in May 1785 when they resolved to allow him £20 a year for 'a labourer',[20] not exclusively a gardener.

Some idea of the Observatory in relation to its environs during Hornsby's term of office is provided by Richard Davis's map of 1797 (Plate 28, p. 55). This is the first city map to fully embrace the Observatory, and its boundary, in serving as the northern edge of the map, also denotes the edge of the built-up area. It shows Jericho as simply a series of enclosed fields, while the only structure close to the line of the meridian mark is the 'New Workhouse' (near the present University Offices).

Although the map may be a good guide to the surrounding area, it gives a less accurate representation of the Observatory itself. The building appears in elevation rather than plan (unusually for a map) and the Observer's House is seemingly omitted altogether.[21] Nonetheless, the apparently oversimplified shape of the drive (though not the single row of trees lining it) is corroborated by Malchair's last drawing of the institution. 'The Observatory as it appears from the principal gate into the grounds, from recollection, July 3rd 1797'[22] (Plate 26, p. 53) seems to be not so much the recreation of a distant memory (seeing that the globe was only fixed in place in 1794 and Mrs Tagg's planting has now assumed some stature) as being the result of Malchair's failing eyesight.

Thomas Hornsby died in 1810 having been prevented by ill health from observing during the last five years of his life. In spite of the labourer's salary being increased in 1807 from £20 to £30 a year 'for keeping the Observatory and the grounds round it clean',[23] further development of the gardens would have to wait for an injection of new blood.

The Observatory and contemporary garden design

As there was something about the completed layout of the grounds of the Observatory which captured the spirit of the age, it would be appropriate to place their development in context.

The most prominent change in garden design during the eighteenth century had been the replacement of formal gardens by those which exhibited the principles of the landscape movement, whose most prolific exponent was Lancelot 'Capability' Brown. Thus, imbued with the movement's sentiments and tenets, *Crokers Dictionary* of 1765 stated:

> In the laying out and planting of gardens, the beauties of nature should always be studied; for the nearer a garden approaches to nature, the longer it will please...The first thing that should present itself to view should be an open lawn of grass, which ought to be considerably broader than the front of the building. If on the sides of the lawn there are trees planted irregularly, by way of open groves, the regularity of the lawn will be broken.[24]

While intended for the architect's perusal:

> There ought always to be a descent of at least three steps from the house to the garden. This will render the house more dry and wholesome, and the prospect on entering the garden more extensive.[25]

The south front of the Observatory as represented in the University Almanack for 1795 perfectly illustrates these precepts (Plate 35, p. 59).

Landscape gardening had become not only the predominant mode of design but had also acquired a status to match the clientele it served (as the Fourth Duke of Marlborough,

proprietor of Blenheim Palace, would have endorsed). The person who stated its claim to artistry most eloquently was Thomas Whately:

> Gardening, in the perfection to which it has been lately brought in England, is entitled to a place of considerable rank among the liberal arts. It is as superior to landscape painting as a reality to a representation. It is an exertion of fancy, a subject for taste; and being released now from the restraints of regularity, and enlarged beyond the purposes of domestic convenience, the most beautiful, the most simple, the most noble scenes of nature are all within its province.[26]

So, whereas our national gardening had previously acknowledged a debt to the Continent in its imitation of French, Dutch and Italian styles, Horace Walpole felt sufficiently confident to write, with some disdain, in 1784:

> Truth, which after the opposition given to most revolutions, preponderates at last, will probably not carry our style of garden into general use on the continent. The expense is only suited to the opulence of a free country ... A flat country, like Holland, is incapable of landscape. In France and Italy, the nobility do not reside much ... at their villas.[27]

Humphry Repton, in his *Enquiry into the Changes in Landscape Gardening* 1806, considered that landscape gardening required interpretation rather than dogma, and that its practitioners needed to employ general rules to each case in order to satisfy what he termed the four 'modern requisites':

> First it must display the natural beauties, and hide the natural defects of every situation. Secondly, it should give the appearance of extent and freedom by carefully disguising or hiding the boundary. Thirdly, it must studiously conceal every interference of art, however expensive, by which the natural scenery is

improved ... And fourthly, all objects of mere convenience or comfort must be removed or concealed.[28]

Robert Hoggar's Oxford map of 1850 (Plate 29, p. 55) indicates the precepts of the landscape movement as they applied to the Observatory:

- A curving drive, to yield an unfolding scene as one circumnavigated the park.
- A strip of woodland around the edge serving as a perimeter belt.
- The grouping of trees and shrubs into clumps.
- An open parkland sweeping right up to the building.
- The placing of the kitchen garden discreetly away from the house and park.

It also illustrates the several compartments into which the grounds, which had started off as an undifferentiated rectangular field, had come to be distinguished, in accordance with Repton's 'modern requisites'.

A considerable part of the site (that became known as the 'Walton Street field') remained largely untouched but served as the permanent pasture for the animals that would, perhaps just during the summer, be led through the connecting driveway into the more gracious surroundings of the Observatory's front lawn. A sunk-fence or ha-ha between the pasture and this park-in-miniature concealed the 'interference of art' by which the separation was achieved, while the belt of trees around the outside of the drive had the required effect of 'disguising or hiding the boundary'.

The park connected discreetly with the stable yard in its north-east corner, so that as 'objects of mere convenience' the stables were removed to an accessible but peripheral part of the site, obscured from the ornamental grounds and from the Woodstock Road by

solid wooden (rather than ornamental iron) gates. The kitchen garden, conveniently located adjacent, had its ground level raised, to judge by the depth of soil, by the surplus earth excavated in the construction of the Observatory. The use of brick to line a wall had long since been recognized as the 'handsomest and most commodious for nailing',[29] and the fact that here it was integral to the wall's construction indicates it must have been made no later than 1776.[30] As if to confirm Wyatt's involvement, the south-facing back wall rose to a greater height than the sides by means of an elegant architectural sweep in the coping stones.

Finally, the area which we enjoy as our main garden was for the private use of the Observer, who planted it according to his personal taste. Although the outline of the lawns was very much that with which we are familiar today, there was no connecting path directly between the stable yard and the Observatory.

The question naturally arises: Who was responsible for the division of the ground, and its laying out? As regards the former, the apportioning of the whole site to the several areas described must be attributed to James Wyatt. It was he who was conversant with the layout of a country house as an estate, and the necessary division of land according to its various functions. Moreover, his own involvement with the Observatory did not end in 1794 but continued sporadically into the early 1800s.

Nonetheless, it is clear from Malchair's drawings, from early maps and Trustees' records that the laying out of the grounds was by no means completed in Wyatt's time, and that it underwent considerable refinement through to the 1820s. So, if Wyatt knew how to design a building and cut up an estate, it took the subsequent involvement of others to bring the garden design to a satisfactory conclusion, thereby confirming Francis Bacon's dictum, in his essay 'Of Gardens' 1625:

that when Ages grow to Civility and Elegancie, Men come to Build Stately, sooner than to Garden Finely: As if Gardening were the Greater Perfection.[31]

The economic basis for the layout of the grounds, and their completion under Abraham Robertson 1811-27

The image of grandeur and opulence we are presented with in the *University Almanack* for 1794 (Plate 35, p. 59) should not distract us from the economic realities that faced the Radcliffe Trustees in their support for the institution. The Observatory had cost them ultimately about five times the original estimate – some £31,661 – and their resultant attitude towards Thomas Hornsby had a bearing on the way that the grounds were to be managed.

The creation of the Observatory had been at Hornsby's initiative. He himself had received no salary from the Trustees in his capacity as Radcliffe Observer but relied for his income upon his role as Radcliffe Librarian and from lecturing. What he received from them were benefits in kind. As the Trustees pointed out in 1799, after he had made a request for the reimbursement of some expenses:

> Ordered that the secretary write to Dr Hornsby to state that as the Trustees had expended so large a sum in building an Observatory and an exceeding good house for that purpose, with an enclosed garden and offices of every description, they were determined not to permit any permanent demand to be entailed on them in future that does not strictly belong to them to discharge.[32]

The 'enclosed garden' for which Hornsby should have been so grateful, was intended to be productive so that no further drain on the Trustees' resources was incurred in its upkeep. It would have been expected, therefore, that the value of produce, both animal and vegetable, would have at least matched the wages of the gardener, although inevitably the equivalent sum does not appear on the balance sheet. From a modern perspective, the idea of the gardens being self-sufficient seems strange, but it served as their underlying rationale for many years.

If the Trustees had reason to believe that Hornsby owed them a debt of gratitude, his successors came with no such sense of obligation, and the relationship changed with the appointment of the first salaried Observer, Abraham Robertson.

One of his first actions was to make a 'Statement of inconveniences at the House belonging to the Observatory'. The Trustees considered his desiderata and ordered that Robertson 'obtain from Mr Hudson a plan and estimate of a lodge to be erected near the outer garden'.[33] The estimate of £150 for a building next to the main entrance, abutting the hospital wall, was approved, and the succession of lodges was thereby initiated.[34]

Following its building, the Trustees' accounts registered some further expenditure on the grounds, with a payment of £22.1s.0d. in 1811 to 'Mr Penson, nurseryman'.[35] No doubt some of the planting was associated with the new lodge. Equally, the park that it gave access to, being the one area that had to be fit for general inspection, took priority. Certainly Mrs Tagg's original planting was now mature, as the 'View of Oxford, from the Gallery of the Observatory' in Ackermann's *History of the University of Oxford* 1814 indicates[36] (Plate 5, p. 13).

In recognition of the improvements that were taking place, and of the quality of work being performed, the salary of the full-time gardener was raised from £30 to £50 a year in 1814.[37] We know that Robertson himself took an active interest in the gardens because the Trustees reimbursed him in 1818 with £20 'towards the expense of improvements to the garden belonging to the Observatory'.[38] It seems that once the public face of the grounds had been made presentable, he turned his attention to the Observer's private garden, for it can hardly have been an accident that the year he was reimbursed for the improvements coincided with the publication of an engraving by T. and G. Hollis of 'The Observatory, Oxford' (Plate 32, p. 57).[39] Instead of a conventional illustration of the south elevation of the Observatory, we are presented with an image of the north front, with the gardeners putting the finishing touches to the flower beds and lawns.

One obstacle remained in the Trustees' way. They did not own the freehold of the site on which they had invested so much time, money and effort. So with some thought as to the permanence of their investment, and perhaps feeling more flush than previously, they now turned to obtaining outright that which was being leased only on a seven year basis from St John's College. After some negotiation, the Act of Parliament necessary to approve the transaction was passed on July 15th 1820[40] and the sum of £1,900 was paid in 1821 to complete the purchase.

Following the acquisition of the freehold, another wave of improvements to the gardens took place. In 1822 further sums totalling £33 were paid to 'Robert Penson, gardener'[41] – this time, apparently, for his skilled labour as much as the supply of plants. The Pensons' reputation as landscapers had been established with the elder Robert's involvement with St John's College during its transition from formal to landscape garden in the 1770s. Although he was still active nearly fifty years later it would appear likely that it was his son, also Robert, who was engaged by the Trustees in the 1820s to help modify the grounds. For this was the moment at which the layout acquired the appearance shown in Hoggar (confirmed in the St John's College estate map 1827[42]). Interestingly, the main garden of St John's, of all the colleges, most closely resembled that of the Observatory in the mid-nineteenth century.

The most prominent change was in the line of the drive from tear-shaped to kidney-shaped. The practical purpose of the change was to include a direct link with the stable yard, and aesthetically, it served to make the entire circuit of the park an harmonious curve. As a final flourish of the landscaper's art, a shrubbery was placed in the foreground of the line of sight from the main entrance to the Observatory to ensure that visitors were briefly tantalized for want of a view of the building until they had progressed a little around the drive.

Stephen Rigaud 1827–39 and his gardener William Stroud

When Stephen Rigaud became Observer in 1827, quite apart from any report that he had to deliver to the Trustees on the state of the institution, he undertook the more mundane task of making an inventory of the Observatory. His list of artefacts made separately from the contents of his house, puts an agreeably domestic perspective on the day-to-day equipment in use. It included: a rolling stone; a water tub on wheels; a hen coop; 24 glass hand lights; a grindstone; two cucumber frames; two iron pig troughs; all the casks and brewing utensils.[43]

The image of noisome farmyard activity which the list engenders, so redolent of a type of Georgian genre painting, serves as a further reminder of the economic side to the grounds' management. Rigaud had at least one gardening book on his shelves, albeit an old one – Richard Bradley's *New Improvements of Planting and Gardening* 1726[44] – which advised him to be careful in his use of poultry manure: 'very hot and full of salts, greatly tending to vegetation'.[45]

Put in the context of the local economy of the time, the element of production was not in any way surprising. Prior to 1832 the area between St Giles church and Summertown was an unenclosed field, let for a variety of agricultural and horticultural purposes. Its appearance towards the southern end was captured in the etching 'Oxford from the North' by J. Whessell 1821 (Plate 33, p. 58).[46] Drawn from a site roughly equivalent to the present Bevington Road, a group of farm workers are seen heaving hay onto a wagon in the foreground. A similar impression of rustic dishevelment beyond the boundaries of the Observatory is created by Joseph Fisher's drawing of the 'Observatory from the north-west' c.1820 (Plate 34, p. 58).[47]

Between these two viewpoints in the 1820s (before the development of Observatory Street) lay an extension of Tagg's nursery, whose proprietor grew fruit trees against the Observatory's boundary wall.[48] So, by 1827, the only indication of the salubrity that was later to engulf north Oxford was the erection of St John's Terrace.

As well as making the inventory, Rigaud kept a record of the money he paid to his assistant observers and the full-time gardener. The surviving receipts reveal, for the first time, his identity. William Stroud 'Rec'd of Mr S. P. Rigaud Esq. the sum of £25 for half year's wages' biannually from March 1828 to September 1838.[49] As Stroud died aged 74 in 1842, and it would have been unlikely for him to have been taken on at a mature age, the probability is that he had worked at the Observatory at least since Abraham Robertson's time. It was probably he, therefore, that had merited the increase in wages from £30 to £50 a year in 1814, and that had acted as 'staffage' for Hollis's engraving, complete with 'a rolling stone'. Stroud should certainly take the credit, along with Robert Penson, for the alterations that took place during the 1820s.

Floriculture and the Victorian era: the gardens under Manuel Johnson 1840-59 and Robert Main 1860-78

By the time of the separation of the role of Radcliffe Observer from Savilian Professor of Astronomy (rendered 'Civilian' by one unknowing Secretary to the Radcliffe Trust[50]) the layout of the grounds had become settled. There had never been many visiting students, and with the removal of the Observer's responsibility from teaching, the place acquired more the air of a private residence, closed to strangers 'unless they have an introduction to the Observer'.[51]

At the time of the first census of 1841 the lodge was occupied by William Stroud's successor, William Quarterman and his wife Caroline, who acted as lodge keeper. They were both in their forties. Quarterman spent most of the years of his employment working under the young and dynamic Observer, Manuel Johnson.

Johnson himself had his work cut out getting the heliometer up and running, fighting proposals for a railway line nearby ('there will be hindrance ...commotion... tremor'[52]) and arguing his case with the Trustees over a pay rise. The final success of this application (which saw his salary double from £300 to £600 in the space of two years, 1853-54) and the newly elevated social status that came with it, led directly to his request to the Trustees for the enlargement of Observer's House. In 1854 his dining room (now a television room) and bedroom above were extended,[53] and the garden in the vicinity enhanced by flower beds.

At about the same time, and out of his own pocket, Johnson paid for a greenhouse to be erected.[54] Its siting in his private rather than the kitchen garden was a reflection of the fact that he wanted its contents, ornamental or cropping, to be in full view of the household and dinner guests (and hence its prominent position today). If Julia Swinburne's watercolour of 1851 is to be believed – of the garden to the south of Observer's House (Plate 36, p. 59) – floriculture was much in evidence within the park as well.

Manuel Johnson died suddenly in 1859 and his successor, the Reverend Robert Main, painted a rosy picture of the gardens in his first 'Report of the Radcliffe Observer to the Board of Trustees' 1861. Not least among his recommendations was the following:

> Under the head of Personal Establishment I may mention William Quarterman, the gardener, an old and very faithful servant of the Establishment. His industry and honesty are both very remarkable, and I would suggest to the Board the propriety of a small addition to his salary. If this would be advanced to £60 per annum it would be a great source of comfort to him and his family.

Less deserving of praise was another member of staff:

> Mr Green is still employed at the Observatory, for the duties of the meteorological department. His conduct has not been unexceptionable, but I hope he has been steadily improving under the discipline and care, which I have found it necessary to use towards him.[55]

Such carefully couched understatement concealed some serious misgivings about Green's reliability and he was dismissed the following year for 'a serious infringement of discipline'. William Quarterman, on the other hand, received the recommended pay rise and the gardens remained worthy of note in 1862:

> With regard to the grounds, I will assume the permission to spend a trifling sum occasionally for the keeping up of the shrubs. On account of the care which has been taken in former years, the grounds have become famed for their picturesque beauty, but the shrubs suffered severely by the hard winter of 1860 and many of them perished.[56]

This was a fair appreciation of the time involved in garden making and the inevitable reverses that climatic extremes put upon the process. The severity of that winter had been recorded by Green before his departure, notably the night of 24th December when the glass minimum plummeted to 0° F (-18° C).[57] *Jacksons Oxford Journal* for Saturday December 29th 1860 remarked upon the conditions:

> The cold was intense on Monday night, and has not been exceeded for very many years, the thermometer ranging in various localities from 3-13 degrees below zero, thus marking from 35-45 degrees of frost.[58]

The Reverend Main may have been a strict employer, but he was naturally sympathetic towards the staff and patients of the Infirmary who wanted to have a dedicated chapel. No doubt because the Radcliffe Trustees had been responsible for the creation of both the Infirmary and the Observatory, they were in a position to negotiate the transfer of a strip of ground at the Observatory's main entrance to accommodate a new chapel, built in 1864.

As a consequence, the Quartermans and their possessions were relocated in a second lodge, erected on the north side of the entrance. The main gate was evidently the one place from which passers-by had a view of the Observatory, for as Main reported:

> The bit of ground adjoining the Chapel of the Infirmary has been planted provisionally; but opportunities will be taken of making it more ornamental, as it is the only part of the grounds which is distinctly visible from the outside.[59]

The building of the chapel and lodge represent two of the few differences in general layout that are evident in a comparison of Hoggar's map of 1850 (Plate 29, p. 55) with the first edition Ordnance Survey map of 1876 (Plate 30, p. 56) but due to the detail in the latter's 1:500 scale we can see minor garden features that were either not recorded or not extant in Hoggar's time. In particular, the Observer's private garden had acquired a number of flower beds scattered about the lawn. This was the proper place to grow them for, as Thomas Whately had long since observed in 1770: 'Minute beauties in general may abound in a garden ... in a park, they are below our notice.'[60]

The flowering of the Observer's garden may be taken as a reflection of local developments. North Oxford was expanding rapidly as a residential suburb at this time and a number of nurseries sprang up to cater for the garden trade, in particular those of William Day (later Gees) by North Parade, and Joseph Bates by the University Parks.

A century earlier, townsfolk had been content to grow the little 'florists' flowers' – auriculas, pansies, pinks etc. – and compete in intimate 'florists' feasts' in inns and coffee houses.[61] However, the huge and continuing influx of new plants from around the globe during the mid-nineteenth century – flamboyant annuals and semi-tropical perennials – led to the pride of place at the Oxford Horticultural Society's grand summer shows being awarded to calceolarias, dahlias, fuchsias and the like. The cultural requirements of the multitude of new plants took some time to be resolved and presented difficulties in the manner in which they should be integrated into garden design.

The Observer's private lawn was never cut up wholesale by the creation of flower beds but it is quite evident that the arrangement of those that were formed was somewhat whimsical, and their effect tended to destroy the unity of the overall design.

It was a devolution into detail that became the undoing of nineteenth century gardening. The perception that additional embellishment led towards clutter and chaos came to be expressed by late Victorian writers, most inimitably by J. D. Sedding in *Garden Craft Old and New* 1891:

> I should be sorry to be so unjust to the modern landscape gardener as to accuse him of caring over-much for flowers, but of his garden-device generally one may fairly say it has no monumental style, no

ordered shape other than its carefully-schemed disorder. It is not a masculine affair but effeminate and niggling: a little park scenery, curved shrubberies, wriggling paths, emphasized specimen plants, and flower beds of more or less inane shape, tumbled down on the skirts of the lawn or drive...[62]

William Quarterman did not live to see his life's work recorded in plan by the Ordnance Survey (nor commented on by Sedding). He had been forced to retire through ill-health in 1874, aged over 80 and, having vacated the lodge for the sake of his successor, died in 1875. His contribution to the gardens of the Observatory was recorded by Main in his report of that year to the Radcliffe Trustees: 'He occupied the post of gardener for nearly 40 years, and his integrity and general usefulness during that period deserves special mention.'[63]

Quarterman would have been unable to work on the numerous mature trees and shrubs during his latter years, which no doubt contributed to the emphasis on flower gardening. With the arrival of a new man it was the upkeep of the mature grounds that came to occupy much of the gardener's time.

Edward Stone 1879-97

There was a gap of over a year between Main's death and Edward Stone's appointment. The absence of a resident Observer for the year 1878-9 provides us with confirming evidence of the economic value of the gardens because it coincided with the one occasion that an entry was made on the credit side of the accounts for 'garden produce', for a sum of £14.3s.3d.[64] The implication is that with no Observer to consume the fruit and vegetables, the surplus produce had to be sold at market and the proceeds returned to the Trustees.

Stone's first report on the state of the Observatory in 1880 was not very encouraging: 'Nothing was working properly.

My first assistant went to Newhaven for a holiday. He has not returned – a presumed drinking bout...'[65]

Staff morale notwithstanding, the indications are that Edward Stone had little time for the gardens, certainly compared to other incumbents of his post, and that the period of his superintendence was a very quiet one. The ledgers record very few purchases during his term of office and his reports to the Trustees merely repeat that 'the grounds are in good order'.[66]

Thomas Jacob, William Quarterman's successor, had been immediately aware upon his arrival in 1874 of the amount of work that needed to be done to the grounds as a whole. Upon Stone's appointment, therefore, he took the opportunity to push for an assistant, and from 1878 the maintenance of the Observatory's grounds became a two-man job, their respective salaries being £50 and £34.10s.0d. a year.

The first task was to attend to the trees. It had been a hundred years since Mrs Tagg had planted the grounds, and the many elms and beeches, as well as more exotic species, were now fully grown. Some were having to be felled for being in a dangerous condition, or lopped for interfering with observations. One of the few reasons for using the historic instruments kept in the Tower of the Winds had, for a long time, been the vantage point it offered for observing phenomena low down in the sky:

> The Observatory is so surrounded with trees that it frequently happens that they are in the way of an object near the horizon, as seen from a position on the same level with the ground.[67]

As a result of the tree work a modest income was to be derived from the sale of timber. A receipt for £1.10s.0d. from C. Bossom in 1887 was recorded for the tops of three trees, for use in his boat business.[68]

Fragmentation and the First World War: Arthur Rambaut 1898-1924

From our perspective, the Observatory was nearing the end of its useful life at the close of the nineteenth century but at the time it appeared to be undergoing a revival. So far from accepting that Oxford and optical astronomy were irreconcilable, Rambaut persuaded the Trustees to undertake a major new investment, and as a result another generation of frustrated star-gazers passed by.

Even at the time, the institution must have appeared something of an anachronism to the outside world. Shut away behind high walls and solid gates (apart from the main entrance), surrounded by buildings on all sides, the soot-blackened, crumbling stonework[69] and overgrown trees must have made the Observatory appear a survival from a distant era. Within, the idyll of the landscape park was fading in the face of reality. The construction in 1894 of a hospital corridor, linking the new men's ward to the old Infirmary, had resulted in the loss of part of the perimeter belt of trees. Instead of a leafy screen terminating the line of sight from the Observatory, Arthur Rambaut found himself looking at something he would rather not have to contemplate:

> Of late I have noticed that the lower sashes of the men's ward in the Infirmary have been thrown up and a full view of the patients in bed and the paraphernalia of the ward, not always of a pleasant character, have become fully visible from the Observatory grounds.[70]

To add to his woes, the wooden posts surrounding the park were becoming as rotten at supporting the double chain fence as they were at retaining cattle, which had 'made their way over and under them'.[71] The post and chain fence was not the only barrier that proved to be defective:

> The wall of the sunk fence which separates the two fields, is in a very dilapidated state.

It has had to be reinforced with iron hurdles in places, to prevent animals in the Walton Street field from straying over the front lawn.[72]

This was the first direct reference to the ha-ha that had been constructed in Hornsby's day to separate the landscape park from the Walton Street field (shown on the First Edition Ordnance Survey map of 1876 as a series of hatched markings around the western edge of the perimeter belt) (Plate 30, p. 56). Further erosion of the park as a landscape entity came in 1902 when it was bisected by a railing thrown across from north to south, next to the heliometer. The eastern portion Rambaut was able to use as 'room for a tennis lawn' and to enjoy 'the shade of the fine trees in front of the house'.[73]

In his private garden, Rambaut had identified failings as soon as he had arrived:

> The greenhouses have not been painted within present memory and are now in such a crumbling condition that new houses would probably cost less than the necessary repairs to the old ones.[74]

His predecessor's lack of interest in the gardens was in stark contrast to Rambaut's own commitment to them. Entries in the accounts grew with the everyday expenditure on plants and garden impedimenta: rose trees, strawberry plants, a magnolia, sea kale plants, flower pots, twine, a small lawn mower (1903-04), a 20 inch lawn mower (1904-05), advertisement for gardener's post...[75]

The last item was occasioned by an event in 1909:

> The gardener, Jacob, died on November 10th. He had been ailing for some weeks when I returned from America on October 4th, and even then it was only with the greatest difficulty that I prevailed on him to go into the Infirmary, where Dr Osler most kindly assented to see him. He suffered acute agony towards the end, but was happily spared a very prolonged illness.[76]

The lodge had been improved a little when Jacob married. For his successor, J. Stonehill, Rambaut ensured that its state of decoration was again adequate:

> Three rooms were cheaply papered, and a little painting done inside and out to make the place cheerful for the new man.[77]

The War brought into sharper relief the conflicting demands placed on land use by astronomy and medicine, and between ornament and utility. Here was an institution struggling to maintain a scientific value, to which end it required the minimum of disturbance and the maximum of space. Adjacent to it the hospital authorities wanted to respond to the huge upsurge in the demands placed upon them, both by the city population and the war injured, by expanding into the apparently under-used grounds next door.

Early in the conflict the Observer saw two members of staff leave that were able to fight (the gardeners exempted as being engaged in a reserved occupation), while as a concession to the hospital 'at the suggestion of Sir William Osler the wounded soldiers in the Infirmary were admitted to the Observatory grounds'. A gate was made in the wall separating the two premises close to St Paul's church in Walton Street, much to the appreciation of the patients, 'of whom several were generally to be seen during the winter afternoons kicking a football at goals erected in the Walton Street field'.[78]

As another contribution to the war effort, Rambaut agreed to 'a request from two of the Doctors at the Radcliffe Infirmary for a plot of ground to plant potatoes and vegetables for the use of the Infirmary'. As they were, unfortunately, 'soon afterwards called up for medical service'[79] Rambaut had his own gardeners continue the job of digging up the lawn in front of Observer's house.

The stables were no longer needed for coaches and a certain air of dilapidation became evident in their appearance, as a contemporary photograph shows (Plate 37, p. 60).[80] There being no further use for animals at the Observatory, the Walton Street field was let out to Mr Crapper, the carrier, for grazing, fruit growing, vegetable cultivation and poultry keeping.[81]

After the War, a return to normality was attempted. The gateway in the wall, made for the benefit of the wounded soldiers, was bricked up, the lawn in front of Observer's House was returfed, the doors separating the institution from the outside world were repaired – and the Observer continued to resist any further intrusion onto the Observatory's grounds. With Rambaut's demise in 1924, however, the Observer's role changed from repelling boarders to jumping ship.

Harold Knox-Shaw, 1924 to the close of the Observatory in Oxford

From the inception of the Observatory right up to the moment of Harold Knox-Shaw's appointment, one of the Observer's roles in the pursuit of astronomy had been to defend the establishment against outside forces – be they robbers, hospital developers, railway magnates, tram operators, chimney builders or cinematograph theatre proprietors (to list some of the people that successive incumbents had to contend with). Knox-Shaw was the first Observer to accept that the pursuit was in vain, and that studying the weather in depth was a poor substitute for observing the heavens under clear skies.[82] So although it was over ten years before the Radcliffe Observatory moved to South Africa, alternative uses for the site were considered early on.

The first surveyor's report was com-missioned of E. J. Brooks in 1925:

> If the Trustees decide in the future that it is necessary or expedient to remove the Observatory outside Oxford the site would be ripe for immediate development and

the value for this purpose lies in the fact that besides having considerable frontage to the important thoroughfares, it gives facilities for an intersecting road of 40 foot in width from Woodstock Road to Walton Street and sufficient depth on each side to offer attractive building plots for which there would be a big demand.[83]

As the accompanying plan indicates (Plate 39, p. 61), the line of the 'intersecting road' ran straight through the site, and the Observatory would have been obliterated in its path. If there appears to be a lack of sentiment for the historic buildings in this report, at the point that the institution had to be moved, the value of its original site was transformed into being merely the means to pay for a new one.

The second surveyor's report of March 1926, from J. Willmott, was more restrained in its judgement, keeping the bisecting road in outline, but recommending the sale only of part of the Walton Street field – and to the Infirmary, rather than to a housing developer. More optimistically, it offered a reprieve for the Observatory:

> In the event of the removal of the Observatory, and the sale of the site, I am of opinion that it will then be found that the site will command as good a price with the existing buildings upon it, as it would if cut up and disposed of as a building estate, and it would then not be necessary to extend the new road.[84]

Willmott's report also, by way of an introduction, described the layout of the gardens and grounds (Plate 40, p. 61):

> The front elevation of the Observatory overlooks the grounds, which have been laid out as a small Park. The north elevation fronts the garden which is attached to the Observer's house. The stable buildings and yard, which are occupied with the Observer's house, are situate between the house and the Woodstock Road.
>
> The Observatory grounds are

bounded on the south and west by a belt of trees in which the new Dome has been erected. This belt forms a good screen to the western boundary of the park-like lands, and between this belt and Walton Street is a field of Pasture land having a frontage of almost 140 yards to Walton Street.[85]

Willmott's description of the grounds of the Observatory would have served almost equally as well over a 100 years earlier, with all the separate elements largely intact. This was the ultimate compliment that could have been paid to the original garden layout and to the many Observers and gardeners who had been responsible for its development and upkeep.

The Observatory gardens and the Nuffield Institute for Medical Research

The progressive development of the hospital to the south and west of the Observatory from the mid-1930s is graphically illustrated in a sequence of plans in Jenny Selby-Green's *History of the Radcliffe Infirmary*.[86] The extent of the 'Garden Piece' of 9 acres 1 rod 3 perches that attached to the Observatory became reduced to about one third of the original area (Plate 31, p. 56), and the retreating boundary led to the construction of Lodge number three (demolished 1989). The Observatory's front lawn was transformed into a car park for the use of the Nuffield Institute for Medical Research.

Had the proposals for the construction of a nurses' home in the former private garden of the Observer been approved in 1948, there would have been virtually no garden left to describe, or for Green College to inherit (Plate 38, p. 60). However, a vigorous and virtuous defence of the one area that remained intact was put up by, among others, A. H. T. Robb-Smith, Nuffield Reader in Pathology, and John Betjeman, then Secretary of the Oxford Preservation Trust. They appealed to readers of *The Times*:

The Radcliffe Observatory at Oxford is threatened with irreparable defacement ... The south frontage has already been built up with brick buildings out of scale and out of texture with the Observatory. It is now proposed to complete the destruction by obscuring the north ...[87]

The scheme was dropped. As Richard Lehman later recounted in the *Oxford Medical School Gazette* of 1974:

Determined opposition, both local and national, helped to avert this despoliation and the grounds remained a pleasure garden as they had been since the eighteenth century.[88]

Not only was there a growing historical appreciation of the architectural value of the buildings, but with the development of Osler House and the use of the premises by the Medical School, the gardens again acquired a significant amenity value:

With the additional provision of sports facilities, they now form one of the attractions of (and distractions from) medical study at Oxford. It is these grounds which now also afford the best setting from which to view what is probably the finest piece of scientific architecture in England.[89]

It was the continued support for the gardens that ensured their survival at the time of the foundation of Green College.

Conclusion

This partial history of the Radcliffe Observatory has been, at one level, a history of the changing values that have attached to its surrounding land.

At the outset, the value of the grounds accorded with the distinguished architecture deemed fit for an eminent astronomer, justifying the creation of a landscape park and all the accoutrements of a small country house.

For as long as the building remained as a functioning observatory, the gardens and grounds were valued as an aesthetic and productive amenity to the Observer, ensuring unimpeded views all around.

The value of the land acquired by the Infirmary from the Observatory was to provide accommodation for its expanding requirements in health provision, whereas the amenity value placed upon the contracted grounds of the Observatory from the 1930s ensured their survival up to the present era.

The gardens that I tend at Green College, at the Radcliffe Observatory (to give it its correct address) are in this history the end of a line of succession which has seen them pass from the Observer, through the Nuffield Institute for Medical Research and the Medical School, to Green College. If, ultimately, the greatest value of land attaches to building development, the future of the gardens 'at the Radcliffe Observatory' will remain dependent on the practical and aesthetic value placed upon the spaces left in between.

Appendix to Chapter 3

Drawings relating to the Radcliffe Observatory by John Baptist Malchair 1729–1812

The principal collections of Malchair's drawings in Oxford are held by the Ashmolean Museum, Corpus Christi College and the Bodleian Library. The Ashmolean Museum's 'Catalogue of Drawings IV Pt. 2 Earlier British Drawings D. B. Brown' (DBB) lists their holding of his work. Colin Harrison's book *John Malchair of Oxford* 1998 on the artist and musician is comprehensive.

The sequence of drawings and etchings may be seen both as a record of the development of the Observatory and its grounds up to the end of the eighteenth century, and as a means of envisaging the buildings in their local environment. The entries are listed in chronological order. A fuller description has been given to those drawings that have not been reproduced in this volume.

Date	Title ('actual' or ascribed), Description, Medium, Source
1763	'North View'. (Plate 23, p. 52). Etching. XII Views consisting chiefly of the environs of Oxford. Bodleian Library Vet A5. c.62 (4).
1773, 23rd June	'Part of Observatory Oxford…1. Observatory 2. Equatorial Sector 3. Hingsey Hill'. An early view of Keene's buildings under construction. Pencil, black chalk and watercolour. Ashmolean Museum DBB 1235.
1774, October	'Near the Observatory'. (Plate 1, p. 11). Pencil and watercolour. Corpus Christi College MS CCC 443 VII (17).
1774, 17th Oct.	'The beginning of the Observatory, Oxford'. (Plate 2, p. 11). Pencil and watercolour. Corpus Christi College MS CCC 443 X (13). Cat. No.19 in John Malchair of Oxford, Colin Harrison 1998.
1776, 28th Dec.	'From the Observatory…Oxford' (Plate 24, p. 52). Grey wash over pencil. Ashmolean Museum DBB 1006.
1777, 14th April	The Radcliffe Observatory under construction, from the SW. Pencil and grey wash. Ashmolean Museum DBB 1010.
1777	'The Observatory at Oxford while abuilding'. From WSW. Pencil and watercolour. Bodleian MS Top. Oxon. b.222. Cat. No. 30 Harrison.
c.1777	The Observatory under scaffolding, similar in date to the preceding entry, but from the NE, the first floor nearing completion (Plate 3, p. 12). Pencil and watercolour. Green College collection.
1778, 9th Jan.	'The Infirmary at Oxford from Professor Hornsby's house at the Observatory'. (Plate 25, p. 53). Pencil and wash. Cat. No. 31 Harrison (lent by Mr and Mrs E A Williams).

Date	Title ('actual' or ascribed), Description, Medium, Source
1778 or '79	The Observatory and Observer's House under construction, from ESE. Building completed to top of tower, with temporary roof covering over. Pencil and watercolour. Ashmolean Museum DBB 1234.
1780, 21st June	'The North Front of the Observatory, Oxford'. A modest drawing made from outside the grounds in pencil and grey wash. Ashmolean Museum DBB 1017 (another version in pencil and watercolour DBB 1019).
1782, 26th June	'By Worcester Coll. Oxon'. Looking up the present Walton Street towards a globeless Tower of the Winds. A fair pencil drawing with grey washes. Ashmolean Museum DBB 1027.
1783, 5th June	'The Observatory at Oxford from Worcester College'. Drawn from the grounds. Pencil and watercolour. Ashmolean Museum DBB 1251.
1784, 20th Dec.	'The place of the Sun's Setting as seen from Professor Hornsby's Dining Parlour at the Observatory at Oxford'. (Plate 27, p. 54). Pencil and watercolour. Ashmolean Museum DBB 1254. (Another version DBB 974).
1786, 24th June	'The Observatory…From the Banbury Road beyond St Giles Church…'. A fine pencil and watercolour drawing. Ashmolean Museum DBB 956. Harrison Cat. No. 52. (Another version of uncertain authorship DBB 1260.)
1792, 30th May	'The Observatory from the Parks'. A slight pencil and wash drawing. Corpus Christi College MS CCC 443 IV (9).
1792, 6th June	'The Tower of the Observatory at Oxford'. A fine drawing in pencil and watercolour made at 8 p.m. and capturing the evening light; the Tower still globeless. Corpus Christi College MS CCC 443 IV (14).
1797, 3rd July	'The Observatory as it appears from the principal gate into the grounds…from recollection'. (Plate 26, p. 53). Dark grey ink and wash. Ashmolean Museum DBB 918. Harrison Cat. No. 95.
Undated	View of the Observatory from the NW. A modest pencil drawing. Ashmolean Museum DBB 1092.
Undated	The Radcliffe Observatory. Viewed from the east at a distance. Ashmolean Museum DBB 1096.

Through his role as drawing master Malchair had many expert pupils within and beyond the University who emulated his subtle style of pencil drawing with colour or grey washes. As a result a number of views of the Observatory of uncertain authorship appear in the Bodleian library's 'Drawings by J B Malchair and pupils' MS Top. Oxon. b.93 (fols.9, 14). A view of the Observatory from the Parks 1798, attributed to Miss Anne Hornsby, is in MS Top. Oxon b.123 (fol.2r).

Notes

1. This is a brief summary of events covered in greater detail in Guest, I. (1991) *Dr John Radcliffe and his Trust*. The Radcliffe Trust, London. 229-30.

2. St John's College (Nov/Dec 1769 and Jan/Feb 1770) Munim V.B.136, Survey of St Giles etc. by Ed. and Thos. Smith.

3. Bodleian Library (1763) John Baptist Malchair, *XII Views consisting chiefly of the environs of Oxford*. Vet A5. c.62: 4.

4. Crossley, A. (ed.) (1979) *A History of the County of Oxford*. Volume IV *The City of Oxford*. Oxford University Press, Oxford. IV: 114.

5. Guest (1991) 242.

6. The name of the road as it appears on Richard Davis's map of 1797. This part of the Woodstock Road was also known as St Giles Road West during the nineteenth century.

7. Oxford, Corpus Christi College. MS CCC 443 (VII) 17.

8. Oxford, Corpus Christi College, MS CCC 443 (X) 13.

9. Marshall, W. (1796) *Planting and Rural Ornament*. 2nd edition. I.

10. Bodleian Library (1771) *Attorney General to Lord Lichfield: Decree authorizing foundation of the Radcliffe Observatory*. MS d.d. Radcliffe c.40.

11. Bodleian Library (15 May 1776) *Trustees Minute Book* 1752-1792. MS d.d. Radcliffe c.51.

12. Bodleian Library (24 February 1776) Trustees Minute Book 1752-1792. MS d.d. Radcliffe c.51.

13. Malchair, J. B. *Drawings of John Baptist Malchair*. Ashmolean Museum DBB no. 1006.

14. Harrison, C. (1998) *John Malchair of Oxford*. Ashmolean Museum, Oxford. Catalogue no.31.

15. The clump is still evident on the 1876 first edition Ordnance Survey map, 1:500 scale.

16. A drawing in Harrison (1998) Catalogue no.35. 'View from the window of Malchair's parlour' (1782) is annotated by Malchair, 'in this Drawing is traced the Meridional Altitude of the Sun at the Winter Solstice'.

17. Malchair, J. B. *Drawings of John Baptist Malchair*. Ashmolean Museum DBB no. 1254.

18. Centre for Oxfordshire Studies, The *Universal British Directory 1790-1798*. Facsimile edition. 113.

19. A photograph in Guest (1991) facing page 432, shows it in a dilapidated state shortly before demolition.

20. Bodleian Library (5 May 1785) MS d.d. Radcliffe c.51.

21. In mitigation, Davis's map was based on a survey made several years earlier.

22. J. B. Malchair, *Drawings of John Baptist Malchair*, Ashmolean Museum, DBB no. 918. The drawing is reproduced in Harrison (1998) Catalogue no.95.

23. Bodleian Library (2 June 1807) MS d.d. Radcliffe c.52.

24. Croker, T. H. (1765) *The Complete Dictionary of Arts and Sciences*. London. Volume 2, under 'Garden'.

25. Croker (1765).

26. Whately, T. (1770) *Observations on Modern Gardening*. London. 1.

27. Walpole, H. (1931) *On Modern Gardening*. Young Books, New York. 69.

28. Repton (1806) *Enquiry into the Changes in Landscape Gardening*. London. 34.

29. Laurence, J. (1726) *The Clergyman's Recreation*. 6th edition. London. 25.

30. Bodleian Library (15 May 1776): the decision to 'enclose the whole premises with a wall'.

31. There are many editions of his essays: e.g. Everyman's Library (1962) *Francis Bacon's Essays*, London. 137-43.

32. Bodleian Library (18th May 1799) MS d.d. Radcliffe c.52.

33. Bodleian Library (9th June 1810) MS d.d. Radcliffe c.52.

34. The building dates of the successive lodges were 1810, 1864, c.1936, and 1978.

35. Bodleian Library (19 June 1811) MS d.d. Radcliffe c.52.

36. Ackermann, R. (1814) *A History of the University of Oxford*. London. II; frontispiece.

37. Bodleian Library (7 June 1814) MS d.d. Radcliffe c.52.

38. Bodleian Library (9 June 1818) MS d.d. Radcliffe c.53.

39. First published in 1818, Hollis's engraving later appeared in Ryman, J. (1839) *Views of Oxford*. Oxford. Illustrations of the Observatory are surveyed by Nick Beeching

in the *Oxford Medical School Gazette* (1978)
XXX: 3: 54-9.

40. Bodleian Library (15 July 1820) MS d.d.
Radcliffe c.40. *Act for enabling the President and
Scholars of St John's College to sell and convey to
the Trustees of the Will of Dr John Radcliffe, a piece
of ground in the Parish of St Giles, and the
Observatory and other buildings thereon.*

41. Bodleian Library (7 June 1822) MS d.d.
Radcliffe c.53.

42. St John's College muniments, MP42, A Map
of the part of St Giles surveyed by John Allen
1827.

43. Museum of the History of Science, Radcliffe
MSS 53, Radcliffe Observatory inventories
etc.

44. An item from his library auctioned by
Sotheby's on behalf of the Radcliffe Trustees
May 7th 1935. A copy of the auction list is in
the Centre for Oxfordshire Studies, OXFU 7
RADCo.

45. Bradley, R. (1726) *New Improvements of Planting
and Gardening*, 5th edition. London. 30.

46. Bodleian Library, Oxford Dep. b.204, No.58.

47. Bodleian Library, MS Top. Oxon. b.89, p.82,
No.120.

48. Bodleian Library (7 June 1814) MS d.d.
Radcliffe c.52: 'Upon reading the application
of Thomas Tagg, a gardener at Oxford,
addressed to the Trustees for permission to
train his fruit trees against the wall of the
Observatory. Ordered that the Secretary do
write to him that such permission is granted
to him during the pleasure of the Trustees.'

49. Museum of the History of Science, MSS
Radcliffe 53, Receipts for salaries and wages
of Observers' assistants.

50. Following Hornsby's request for the
reimbursement of his expenses in 1799, the
Trustees finally agreed to pay his Window,
House, Militia and Gaol Taxes: 'It was resolved
he would be allowed the same in future during
his life, or so long as he be continued Civilian
Professor'. Bodleian Library (15 June 1799)
MS d.d. Radcliffe c.52.

51. The Observatory never had the same public
access as other University buildings, as this
quotation indicates: from Munday and Slatter
(1820) *The Oxford University and City Guide.*
Oxford. 119.

52. Bodleian Library (1853) MS d.d. Radcliffe
c.40. Objections to the Proposed Railway
from Tring to Oxford.

53. Bodleian Library (20 June 1854) MS d.d.
Radcliffe c.54: 'Ordered that a bay window be
made to the dining room of the dwelling
house at the Observatory and a glass covering
to the lobby on the upper floor.'

54. No entry in the Trustees' accounts appears at
the time of Johnson's purchase, but they agreed
to reimburse his widow for part of its cost:
'Ordered that £20 be paid to Mrs Johnson, the
present value of the greenhouse erected in the
Observatory grounds by her late husband.'
Bodleian Library (15 July 1862) MS d.d.
Radcliffe d.38.

55. Bodleian Library (1861) G.A. Oxon c.228,
*Reports of the Radcliffe Observer to the Board of
Trustees 1861-64.*

56. Bodleian Library (15 July 1862), MS d.d.
Radcliffe d.38.

57. Main, R. (1862) *Results of the Meteorological
Observations made in the year 1860*, Oxford. 74.
Published in *Astronomical and Meteorological
Observations made at the Radcliffe Observatory, in
the years 1859, 1860.* XX. Oxford.

58. *Jackson's Oxford Journal* (29 December 1860) 5.

59. Bodleian Library (1865) Per.184 d.57. *Reports
of the Radcliffe Observer 1863-1877.*

60. Whately (1770) 158.

61. *Jackson's Oxford Journal* in the late eighteenth
century records several of these meetings
at The Mitre and Mr Darlington's Coffee
House.

62. Sedding, J.D. (1891) *Garden Craft Old and New.*
London. 72n.

63. Bodleian Library (1875) Per.184 d.57. *Reports
of the Radcliffe Observer 1863-1877.*

64. Bodleian Library (1878-9) MS d.d. Radcliffe
c.43. *Radcliffe Observatory Accounts.*

65. Bodleian Library (1880) MS d.d. Radcliffe
c.40. *Observer's Reports.*

66. Bodleian Library (e.g. 1881, 1893, 1897) MS
d.d. Radcliffe c.40, *Observer's Reports.*

67. Bodleian Library (1872) Per.184 d.57. *Reports
of the Radcliffe Observer 1863-1877.*

68. Bodleian Library (1887-8) MS d.d. Radcliffe
c.44. *Radcliffe Observatory Accounts 1870-1898.*

69. Bodleian Library (1897) MS d.d. Radcliffe
c.40. *Observer's Report:* 'A fragment weighing

seven and a half pounds recently fell from the ornamental carved work of the Tower'.

70. Bodleian Library (1900) MS d.d. Radcliffe c.40. *Observer's Report*.

71. Bodleian Library (1898) MS d.d. Radcliffe c.40. *Observer's Report*.

72. Bodleian Library (1912) MS d.d. Radcliffe d.41. *Observer's Report*.

73. Bodleian Library (1902) MS d.d. Radcliffe d.41. *Observer's Report*.

74. Bodleian Library (1898) MS d.d. Radcliffe c.40. *Observer's Report*.

75. A short selection of items taken from Bodleian Library (1898-1912) MS d.d. Radcliffe c.43. *Radcliffe Observatory Accounts*.

76. Bodleian Library (1910) MS d.d. Radcliffe d.41. *Observer's Report*.

77. Bodleian Library (1910) MS d.d. Radcliffe d.41. *Observer's Report*.

78. Bodleian Library (1915) MS d.d. Radcliffe d.41. *Observer's Report*.

79. Bodleian Library (1917) MS d.d. Radcliffe d.41. *Observer's Report*.

80. Bodleian Library (1974) MS d.d. Radcliffe d.43, f.8.

81. Bodleian Library (1918) MS d.d. Radcliffe d.41. *Observer's Report*.

82. Knox-Shaw felt that the meteorological observations 'no longer justified the amount of time and energy that was being spent on them. They had served their purpose in providing us with an accurate knowledge of the climate of Oxford'. Bodleian Library (1925) MS d.d. Radcliffe d.41. *Reports of the Radcliffe Observer*.

83. Bodleian Library (10 February 1925) MS d.d. Radcliffe c.40. Brooks, E. J. *Report on the future of the Radcliffe Observatory*.

84. Bodleian Library (20 March 1926) MS d.d. Radcliffe c.40. Willmott, J. *Report re disposal of land between Observatory and Walton Street*.

85. Bodleian Library (20 March 1926) MS d.d. Radcliffe c.40. Willmott, J. *Report re disposal of land between Observatory and Walton Street*.

86. Selby-Green, J. (1990) *The History of the Radcliffe Infirmary*. Image Publications, Banbury, Oxon. 145-8.

87. Robb-Smith, A. H. T. *et al.* (18 March 1948) Radcliffe Observatory. Letter to *The Times*.

88. Lehman, R. (1974) The Radcliffe Observatory, *Oxford Medical School Gazette*. 23.

89. Lehman (1974).

Plate 23. 'North View', etching by J. B. Malchair 1763, showing the north façade of the Radcliffe Infirmary with, in front, the garden plot on which the Observatory was to be built
(*Bodleian Library, Oxford*)

Plate 24. 'From the Observatory, December 28th 1776' pencil drawing by J. B. Malchair, in the year that the grounds were first planted, looking south-east from Observer's House to the main entrance, opposite the Royal Oak (*Ashmolean Museum, Oxford*)

Plate 25. 'The Infirmary at Oxford, from Professor Hornsby's house, January 9th 1778', watercolour by J. B. Malchair. The hospital's outbuildings are disguised by some recent planting in the grounds of the Observatory. In Colin Harrison, *John Malchair of Oxford* (*courtesy of Mr and Mrs E. A. Williams*)

Plate 26. 'The Observatory as it appears from the principal gate into the grounds, from recollection July 3rd 1797' by J. B. Malchair (*Ashmolean Museum, Oxford*)

Plate 27. 'The place of the sun's setting as seen from Professor Hornsby's dining parlour at the Observatory, December 20th 1784', pencil and watercolour by J. B. Malchair. An uninterrupted view towards Hinksey Hill, and the Equatorial telescope house in sparsely furnished grounds (*Ashmolean Museum, Oxford*)

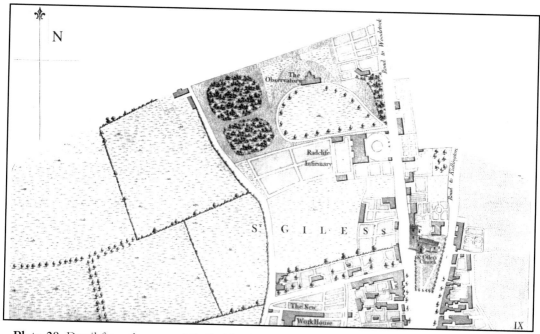

Plate 28. Detail from the map of Oxford by Richard Davis, 1797, showing the Observatory on the fringe of the city

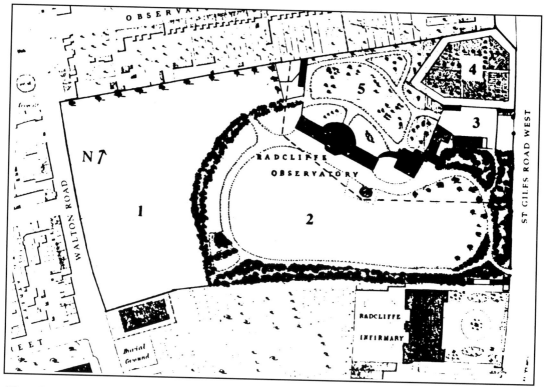

Plate 29. Detail from the map of Oxford by Robert Hoggar, 1850. The five compartments into which the grounds of the Observatory were divided are marked: (1) pasture, (2) park, (3) stable yard, (4) kitchen garden, and (5) Observer's private garden

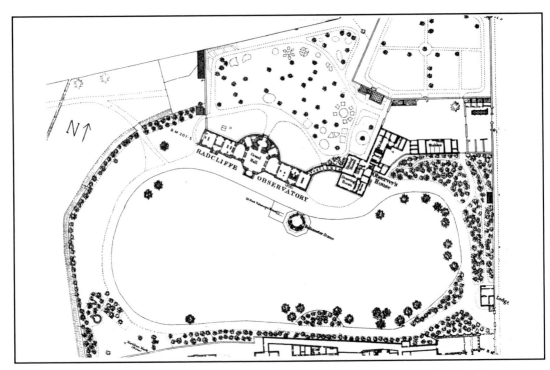

Plate 30. Detail from the First Edition Ordnance Survey map 1876, 1:500 scale

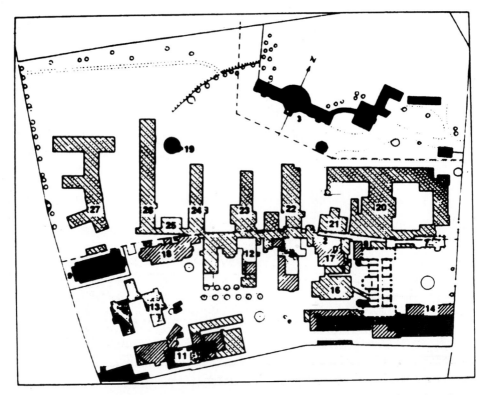

Plate 31. Plan of the Radcliffe Infirmary and the Observatory 1939, showing the reduced extent of the Observatory grounds (*Image Publications, Banbury*)

Plate 32. 'The Observatory, Oxford' engraved by T. and G. Hollis, 1818 and published in 1836 (*Green College, Oxford*)

Plate 33. 'Oxford from the North,' etching by J. Whessell, 1821. North Oxford in its agricultural setting as St Giles' Field, prior to enclosure in 1832 (*Bodleian Library, Oxford*)

Plate 34. 'The Observatory from the north-west', drawn by Joseph Fisher c.1820
(*Bodleian Library, Oxford*)

A South View of the Observatory.

Plate 35. The Radcliffe Observatory depicted in the University Almanack, 1794
(*Green College, Oxford*)

Plate 36. 'The garden setting of the Observatory to the south-east', watercolour by Julia Swinburne,
1851 (*Green College, Oxford*)

Plate 37. The stables at the end of the coaching era, 1900
(*The Bodleian Library, Oxford, courtesy The Radcliffe Trust*)

Plate 38. 'The Radcliffe Observatory at Oxford, with the land on which it is proposed to build a home for nurses, thereby obscuring the view of the north frontage' (*The Times*, 18th March 1948)

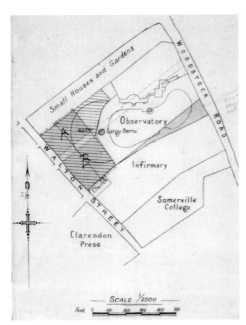

Plate 39. Plan included in the report on the future of the Radcliffe Observatory, E. J. Brooks, 1925. A bisecting road for a projected housing development would run straight through the middle of the building (*The Bodleian Library, Oxford, courtesy The Radcliffe Trust*)

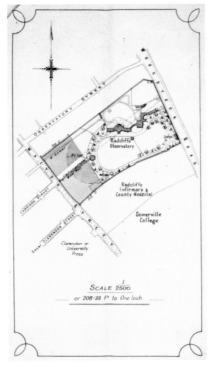

Plate 40. Plan included in the surveyor's report on the Observatory by J. Willmott 1926. A more modest proposal, highlighting the continuity of the layout of the grounds from the early nineteenth century to the end of the Observatory's occupation of the site
(*The Bodleian Library, Oxford, courtesy The Radcliffe Trust*)

Chapter 4

Astronomical Measurement at the Radcliffe Observatory 1773-1934

Roger Hutchins

Chapter One explained how the University's Savilian Professor of Astronomy, Thomas Hornsby (1733–1810), astutely recognized that the imminent completion of the Radcliffe Infirmary presented the opportunity to petition the Trustees of Dr John Radcliffe's Trust to provide a new observatory for the University's and thereby for his own use. It was also explained why, on what was then a greenfield site at the north edge of the city, the building was aligned on an east to west axis, and that while one wing was equipped for research, Hornsby's innovation was that the other wing should be specifically for teaching. Hornsby and his family moved in to the Observer's House in 1773, and had immediate access to the nearest end of the nearby main building which housed the principal instruments. As to the other facilities, the Lecture Room on the first floor was only completed in 1789, and apparently only furnished in 1797. The Observing Room above it, which was to accommodate the portable instruments used for observing beyond the meridian, was only completed in all respects by 1795. That was of little importance to Hornsby, as his principal work would be with the three instruments needed to observe stars as they crossed the celestial meridian. When finally completed in 1795 the Radcliffe Observatory, because it

also contained the best state-of-the-art suite of research instruments, was beyond doubt the finest observatory in Europe.

Hornsby's aspirations and motivation are the first pivot of the building's history – the second is the removal of the astronomical work to South Africa in 1934-5. Hornsby started his working life as an Oxford academic in the mid-eighteenth century. Astronomy had entered a particularly exciting era, emerging as the first applied science of the Enlightenment. This came about because observations of the movements of the Moon and planets against the background stars, examples of what is now called celestial mechanics, presented physical phenomena that required explanation, and the explanatory theories evolved by applying a new mathematics. Reliable prediction of the angular positions of the Sun and Moon in relation to the position of an observer ashore or at sea were crucial to navigation and made developments in astronomy central to safety at sea and therefore essential to exercising Britain's maritime power; mathematics could thereby make an increasing claim for intellectual status at England's two universities. The founding of the Radcliffe Observatory at Oxford was a direct result of Hornsby's initiatives, within the context of the special conditions of his Oxford chair, and the tradition he inherited.

Sir Henry Saville's enlightened statutes precluded incumbents of the Savilian chairs of Astronomy and of Geometry from holding clerical livings. This restriction had the invaluable result that the Chairs were actually effective in advancing research and teaching, and were usually held by distinguished men. Among them, between 1705 and 1760 which was a crucial period in the development of astronomical instruments and methods, were Edmond Halley (1656–1742, a graduate of the Queen's College) who groomed James Bradley (1693–1767, of Balliol College). Both men held the post of Astronomer Royal at the Royal Observatory, Greenwich (hereafter ROG) simultaneously with the Savilian chair. Halley also trained Nathaniel Bliss (1700–64), who would succeed Bradley at Greenwich. In that era before astronomy became characterized by large quantities of data and an organized division of labour, two essential qualities for astronomical research were individual flair and the ability to effect the direct transfer of observing skills. By their regular presence to lecture, Halley and Bradley made Oxford an astronomical centre of excellence and aspiration. The Savilian stipend was only £130 per year but Bradley also developed the lucrative teaching of Natural Philosophy in the Ashmolean Museum on Broad Street (now the Museum of the History of Science). Hornsby was Bradley's pupil, so was well aware of what might be achieved.[1]

Several Oxford men were founders of the Royal Society of London, created in 1662 to further the pursuit of natural knowledge. Christopher Wren, a graduate of Wadham College in 1651, wrote the preamble to the Society's statutes in which one of the stated aims was to be the development of methods to determine longitude. His colleague, Robert Hooke, who had graduated from Christ Church in 1655 had a special interest in clocks and their application to the longitude problem. Then in 1687, Isaac Newton's laws of universal gravitation were a dramatic revelation to the philosophers, making it possible to analyze and predict the movements and orbits of celestial bodies by mathematical description, the results of which were verifiable by observation.

One consequence of this advance in mathematical theory was the founding in 1675 of the Royal Observatory at Greenwich specifically 'for finding out of the longitude for perfecting Navigation and Astronomy'.[2] This investment by government reflected an increasingly acute problem. Since the fifteenth century international trade by sea had been expanding, and was becoming tremendously valuable. By the seventeenth century Britain, Spain, France and Holland competed to dominate long distance trade, and to achieve prestige and military advantage. Surveyors or mariners could easily calculate with considerable accuracy their latitude, their position north or south of the equator measured in degrees and minutes of angle where one degree equated to 60 miles per degree upon the surface of the Earth or sea. They had only to measure the angle between the Sun when it was overhead at local noon time and the horizon and correct the angle by reference to tables which provided the proper angle by allowing for the date and therefore seasonal tilt of the Earth upon its axis.

However, navigators had no reliable means of calculating longitude – how far east or west they had travelled. It was well known that a difference of one hour in time equated to fifteen degrees of longitude, and that one degree equated to 69 miles at the equator, tapering to 60 miles at 30 degrees and to 45 miles at 50 degrees north or south of the equator; but there were no clocks available that could maintain accurate time at sea and thus provide the essential 'base-line element' for the calculation, the time at Greenwich. This uncertainty in east–west mileage meant that mariners could not be sure of their distance from the actual position of features and hazards along a coastline. The inaccuracies became life-threatening hazards because on long voyages longitude could only be calculated by 'dead reckoning', estimating position by assessing the speed of the ship and miles travelled in 24 hours and then making allowance for the effect of currents and wind. The inevitably accumulating errors led to an ever greater risk of running ashore, and each year many ships were lost along with most of their crews. The risks were dramatically impressed upon parliament and public in 1707 when, after 19 days in fog, part of the British fleet under Admiral Sir Clowdisley Shovell ran ashore on the Scilly Islands with the loss of four ships and nearly 2,000 men just south of the English coast. In 1714 the House of Commons was petitioned by:

> several Captains of Her Majesty's Ships, Merchants of London, and Commanders of Merchantmen ... That the Discovery of the Longitude is of such Consequence to Great Britain, for Safety of the Navy, Merchant Ships, as well as Improvement of Trade, that for want thereof, many ships have been retarded in their Voyages, and many lost.[3]

The Government responded by forming a Board of Longitude which included the Astronomer Royal and the Professors of Astronomy of Oxford and Cambridge Universities, and demonstrated their seriousness by advertising an enormous prize of £20,000 (several million pounds in current value) for a successful solution. An important step forward was the invention in 1731 of the reflecting octant, a simple instrument to measure angles. Based upon this, in 1757 Captain John Campbell (1720–90) invented the marine sextant, a superb instrument capable of determining angles with great precision from the deck of a ship. The determination of longitude now required the invention of an accurate marine chronometer (clock) to provide the other crucial element in the calculation of longitude. This the genius John Harrison (1693–1776) achieved in 1761,

although the cost and complexity of the instrument meant that it did not become generally available for some time.

While slow progress was made in addressing two elements of the longitude problem – making accurate measurements of the angle to the Sun, Moon, or the Pole Star from a moving deck, and determining the difference between local and Greenwich time with increasing accuracy – the equally important third requirement was the mathematical solution applied by the navigator to convert his observations to a real position on a chart. This required the regular publication and availability of accurate astronomical almanacs, books which tabulated the positions of those principal celestial bodies in relation to the Earth for the dates of the year. These positions were found by astronomers measuring them in relation to the reference points of bright background stars. Therefore, once reliable marine chronometers did become available in the late 1700s, the emphasis shifted back to the need for accurate and up to date astronomical almanacs as the other basic tool for precise navigation. Arguments for the public benefit to be derived from the use of meridian or position observing instruments, and the timely reduction and publication of the observations to render them useful, became the principal *raison d'être* for any public astronomical observatory. The need for precision inspired James Bradley to make important innovations in both instrument design and observing method, so that by about 1760 he had improved the accuracy of observations by ten times compared to the standards of 1690, and this made the ROG and its instruments a model observatory.[4] As Dr Alan Chapman has pointed out, before the rise of astrophysics in the late 1800s, all the most important problems – scientific, geodesy and navigation – could be attacked by increasingly precise meridian measurement. However, the most accurate observations over a period of years are of no use whatever unless they are 'reduced' (i.e. mathematically adjusted for several carefully determined instrumental or atmospheric errors, and to a standard time and date), published, and made available in usable form comparable to similar observations made at other observatories.

For those reasons, any assessment of the work of the Radcliffe Observatory and the contribution of its individual directors between 1773 through to 1900 (when meridian work ceased) must reflect the contribution to that corporate effort. Comparison can be made to the standards of accuracy and of timely publication set by a succession of Astronomers Royal, and to similar work at other major national or public observatories. Such comparison includes consideration of the personnel resources needed to publish meridian work, as well as means to purchase new instruments that would ensure precision as instrument technology improved. These two criteria frustrated many directors of observatories. For example, several of the Astronomers Royal before 1835, despite the later ones employing assistants, failed to publish their observations and they thus contributed little to navigation. In this most important function the ROG failed during the directorships of Halley and Bradley, as well as the short lived Bliss and the less able John Pond. By 1811–18 the low repute of the *Nautical Almanac* upon which mariners depended for their calculations spawned the public criticism that exposed the weakness of the ROG and led directly to the founding of the Astronomical Society of London in 1820 (which in 1831 became the Royal Astronomical Society).

The founders of the Society considered it a scandal that the initiative in publishing accurate tables had been snatched by Frederich Bessel at the new Konigsberg University Observatory of 1813. He had adopted the Greenwich model of instruments and observing method, but set new standards for achieving precise measurement, and also devised standard constants for the correction of raw observations by applying Bradley's discoveries of aberration, nutation and refraction. Bessel set a standard for accuracy and for reduction and publication.

Addressing these issues of maritime safety, public utility, and internationally competitive claims to scientific excellence, the Astronomical Society immediately became the pressure group for reform and soon established itself as the specialist forum that offered the coveted rewards of recognition and national and international honours to astronomers. One result of this movement for reform was the founding of the Cambridge University Observatory in 1824.[5] Coincidentally a young Cambridge graduate George Biddel Airy (1801–92) had the rare aspiration to become a professional scientist. Being appointed Director of the Cambridge Observatory in 1828 gave him the choice of work to be pursued there. He realized that by adopting the Astronomical Society's criteria for accuracy of methods and prompt publication of observations he could gain the members' powerful influence, expose the shortcomings at Greenwich, and make himself the only plausible successor there. Airy duly became the immensely influential Astronomer Royal for the half century from 1835 to 1880, during which time his innovations established the ROG as an international model for an effective observatory which employed unskilled labour using standard forms to reduce and publish its observations every year.[6] He thus set a standard of good practice for public utility (thereby justifying his resources), dominated British and much European meridian astronomy, and also became a patron and occasional critic of other observatories including the Radcliffe.

Meanwhile, Halley's and Bradley's astronomical discoveries were proofs of Newtonian gravitation and consolidated the intellectual status of mathematics, not least in the evolving curriculum at Cambridge University. The entirely new potential for accurately measuring celestial positions by meridian observations resulted from Bradley's combination of discovering the variables of aberration and nutation which affected the Earth as an observing platform, his designing instruments with less variable errors, and his making possible methods of reduction that included all those factors. As Savilian Professor he discussed and taught these principles at Oxford. However, these developments were paralleled elsewhere by discoveries which began to open new special areas of astronomical study beyond the meridian, and gradually these would offer a choice of work to directors of university observatories such as the Radcliffe. From his home in Bath, William Herschel in 1786 had discovered the planet Uranus and had thereby secured the King's favour and a pension. Then at the Royal Observatory in Palermo in 1801 Guiseppe Piazzi (1746–1826) discovered the first minor planet (asteroid) which he named Ceres. These discoveries provided all astronomers with the choice of an alternative to meridian work, to use telescopes for the less onerous irregular observations of celestial bodies in any part of the sky. Observing with a refracting telescope from London in the 1820s, John Herschel's proof of the binary nature of the orbits of some double stars extended Newton's laws to distant stellar systems, and thus enabled astronomers to convince the public that their discipline was the first applied science. The new branches of astronomy now increasingly attracted both practitioners and patrons seeking the recognition and honours both of governments and of the Astronomical Society.

It is thus no surprise that on the continent astronomy was very much part of Enlightenment thinking because it offered examples of special problems and solutions susceptible to the new analytical mathematics, calculus, and thus for some became a means to challenge the dogma of the Church. Many British and European intellectuals developed a growing interest in astronomy as part of the metamorphosis of 'natural philosophy' into 'science' during the nineteenth century. In Britain, astronomy became the science that attracted an unparalleled level of private patronage. By the 1830s British amateurs led the world in observational astronomy beyond the meridian.

Enthusiasts within universities began to capitalize on these new possibilities in order to promote some overdue innovation. After the founding of the ROG at Greenwich in 1675, the Radcliffe Observatory became the second astronomical institution; then Trinity College, Dublin completed the Dunsink Observatory in 1787. Reformers at Cambridge University recognized that the national need for improved navigation presented an ideal justification for introducing reforms in to the University, first by adopting the new continental analytical mathematics, then by commitment to build an observatory to support the theoretical work. Despite determined opposition, a new observatory was completed at Cambridge in 1824. Airy successfully made it his stepping stone to the appointment at Greenwich. Glasgow University had had a modest observatory since 1757, and completed a new one outside the city in 1841, and even the new clerical University of Durham built a small observatory in 1840.

However, it was one thing to build an observatory, and to give the direction of it to a professor of mathematics so as to avoid the need for a director's salary. It was quite another matter to decide whether the work of the observatory should be integrated with the curriculum, and whether the professor's research was to be more than his private interest and thus of concern to and to be financed by the university; was the university to bear the cost of the relatively rapid technological redundancy of very expensive instruments?[7] Unlike the situation at the other universities which owned their observatories, it is a defining characteristic in the history of astronomy at Oxford that 'The Oxford Observatory' as the Radcliffe soon became known, remained privately owned and therefore did not attract significant external benefactions. Therefore the key issues of the tension between the Professor–Director's teaching and private research, the provision of a budget for research (including the stipend of an assistant), and instrument renewals, became particularly acute at Oxford.

Hornsby made his first observations from the incomplete Radcliffe Observatory in 1773. Full of enthusiasm, his vision for the work of the observatory having been published and unchallenged in the University, everything seemed possible. One hundred and fifty years later, in the 1920s, his successor found it impossible to continue first class observational research at Oxford, and supervised the closure in 1934 and removal of the Radcliffe Observatory to South Africa in 1935. The 161 year history of the Radcliffe Observatory as an institution for astronomical research is not at all one of smooth progress. In seeking to understand the difficulties and possibilities for astronomy experienced by those who lived and worked in the splendid buildings it is helpful to recognize that science is a socially and culturally organized activity. Therefore the following sections consider the work of the Observatory through the experience of the directors. Each of them had to reconcile the constraints of their instruments against the opportunities of new technology, costs, scientific value, and available resources of funds and labour. A director might be very anxious to embrace advances in instrument power or a research opportunity created by the division of scientific labour increasingly determined by the metropolitan learned societies and by international competition. The directors had however to negotiate with the Trustees for any advance at the Observatory, while even after the schism between the Trust and the University in 1839 they lived and worked among the professors of natural science of the great University which for so many decades appeared oblivious to the prestigious institution at its rural periphery.

Three Professors: 1773–1839

The director of any university observatory inevitably encountered difficulties in establishing the role of his institution. It was one thing to attract capital funding to establish an observatory, much more difficult to obtain an annual sum to pay for an assistant and for research expenses, and another matter altogether to achieve relevance either to the curriculum and to students or to the local or national need. Then, until the twentieth century, pensions were so unusual that it was normal for men to work until their health collapsed. Therefore the scientifically significant activity of an observatory inevitably varied in a cycle as the incumbent declined and/or instruments became obsolete, or patrons waited to equip a new incumbent with a new instrument in order to render him and the observatory effective once again.

For the science of astronomy the Oxford hero is not John Radcliffe, who never intended a penny for astronomy, but Thomas Hornsby, Savilian Professor from 1763–1810, whose initiative in achieving the building of the Radcliffe Observatory has been related elsewhere in great detail.[8] Broadly, there were four consequential results. First, was the construction of the largest university building for research and the practical teaching of natural science anywhere. Second, because of the rhetoric Hornsby used to achieve the foundation, and because it was a modern symbol in Oxford University, the Observatory became first an exemplar, and later the locus of important posts in a new scientific profession. Third, here was the crucially important circumstance of the foundation by which the Trust retained ownership of an observatory built for the University. With hindsight this can be seen as responsible for the operation of the Observatory being seriously compromised for at least half a century during a period of astronomy's dramatic advance and specialization until the Observatory was thoroughly modernized in 1902. Fourth, that issue of ownership inadvertently blighted the development of astronomy in Oxford University both in 1839, and again between 1902 and 1930.

Hornsby succeeded Bradley in the Savilian Chair of Astronomy in 1763 and in the same year was also appointed to the chair of experimental philosophy. The University was poor, and the lack of any adequate facilities for observing one of the pair of very rare transits of Venus (as predicted by Halley) in 1761 illuminated his plight. He observed the first transit from the Earl of Macclesfield's private observatory at Shirburn Castle near Oxford. In 1763 Hornsby published in the Transactions of the Royal Society a detailed discussion of the results of the several international observing expeditions in 1761. Very precise observations of the duration of the transit of Venus across the disk of the Sun, made from widely separated observing stations, offered an opportunity to determine one of the key measurements of distance within the solar system, the distance from the Earth to the Sun. Hornsby concluded that the second of the transits due in 1769 could yield that measurement to an accuracy within one per cent. It is for that reason that Lieutenant James Cook set sail for Tahiti in 1768 as a well publicized element in the Royal Society's plan for the British effort, to which the King promised to contribute £4,000.[9] Hornsby managed to observe the transit from Oxford, and derived a good measurement; but meanwhile he had aspired to use the national interest in the forthcoming internationally competitive venture to put astronomy in Oxford on to the map. In 1768 Hornsby privately sought the support of Lord Lichfield,

who was Chancellor of the University as well as being the Chairman of the Radcliffe Trustees. Having persuaded Lichfield of his plan, he sought academic support by publishing a note in the University:

> That I might ... endeavour to be as useful in this place as possible ... to read a course of Lectures in Practical Astronomy; which I was the rather disposed to undertake as it had never been publikly [sic] attempted in any University.[10]

Having secured support 'from Heads of Houses and other leading members of the University', Hornsby formally petitioned the Trustees citing his statutory duty to: 'make astronomical calculations both by night and by day', using a set 'of the best Instruments that can be provided'.[11] He asked the Trustees to meet 'this noble design' by building 'a large and proper Observatory ... and they will do themselves the highest honour and derive a very considerable benefit to the University and to Mankind'.[12] The petition was made early in 1768. To make the plan workable he needed an assistant. He ingeniously proposed that the colleges should share only the provision of an assistant's salary, and in return send one student each per year for free instruction, while any college member would have access for making observations. He explicitly separated research from teaching, stating that to make the observations sufficiently precise to 'promote the improvement of this science' he would need a separate set of smaller teaching instruments in a different building.[13] Hornsby shrewdly promised all things: to teach two classes a year of practical astronomy, to research and print the observations each year thus making them of public utility, and to embellish the University with a prestigious modern institution.

It was a well conceived plan that would cost the University nothing. Building commenced in June 1772. Lord Lichfield intervened to secure a more prestigious design, but there was only one British instrument maker with the skills to make the instruments, the ageing John Bird (1709–76). Hornsby urgently needed to order and finance the instruments, and the persuasive rhetoric of his lobbying is revealed to us when in February 1771 he circulated a plea to Convocation to support a bridging loan:

> In consideration of the great advantages that may be derived to mankind in general from Observations carefully made with such accurate instruments, and from the farther extension of astronomical knowledge, and also of the honour that will from these redound to the University of Oxford in particular, the Savilian Professor of Astronomy, who has no other point in view, than the promoting of these valuable ends, and the prosecution of the Duties of his Office...[14]

Hornsby secured the loan, and just managed to beat the ROG in ordering what was likely to be the craftsman's last set of instruments. As evidence of the good relationship they developed, Hornsby even persuaded Bird against all his own inclinations to include achromatic object glasses in each instrument. This turned out to be crucial in giving the instruments longevity.

In 1773 Bird delivered the two mural quadrants with focal length of eight feet. These were followed in 1774 by a transit instrument of four inches aperture, and a zenith sector telescope of 12 feet focal length. The total cost was £1,300. For observing beyond the meridian, an equatorial Sector with a 5 foot telescope was completed after Bird's death, and installed beneath a cylindrical revolving dome in the grounds (Plate 27, p. 54); it was never very good, considered 'useless' by 1830 and its 'house' was demolished in about 1920.[15]

At the Observatory a covered way led from the Observer's House to the east wing and the principal instruments. In the easternmost room were mounted the two great mural quadrants of eight feet radius, each rigidly fixed to a small wall aligned north to south, one instrument facing north, the other south (Plate 8, p. 16). The zenith sector instrument was mounted in the small adjacent room to the north. That room opened on to the room where the pivoted transit instrument of eight feet focal length was mounted on its two great piers. Beyond the transit room was the library, and then the central hall below the tower. On the first floor of the tower was the lecture room, with two side rooms for storing apparatus. Above was the octagonal observing room with its large windows and balcony and two refractors by Dollond, one of $4\frac{1}{2}$ inches aperture and 10 feet focal length, and another of $3\frac{1}{2}$ inches aperture and $3\frac{1}{2}$ feet focal length. Later it also housed a movable reflecting telescope by Herschel of 10 feet focal length (Plate 6, p. 14). The western wing contained Hornsby's own small quadrant and his transit instrument, both by Bird, which were now assigned for student use.

Hornsby's appointment to his second chair in 1763 enabled him to marry Ann Cherrill in August of that year, and between 1764 and 1783 they had 12 children of whom seven died in infancy. He moved into the Observer's House in 1773. He supervised the installation of the instruments, and began observing. During any year, the rotation of the Earth each night, and the passage of the months, would successively bring a large number of suitably bright stars slowly 'ascending' from east to west to pass across the long aperture slits in the roof above the transit instrument and the quadrants. The astronomer would have a pre-prepared list of the stars that he wished to observe during the year, and to re-observe another year in order to check the accuracy of the observation, and any variations in the instrument. For each month he would have a working or subsidiary list of those selected stars that would cross the slit at known times during the evening hours. Hornsby made observations of both co-ordinates of a star as it crossed the meridian. First, he used the mural quadrant to measure the star's position in north to south latitude in the sky, known as its 'angle of declination'. He made this measurement by observing the star crossing the first two of five vertical wires in the eyepiece of the mural quadrant, which, as the star traversed a horizontal central wire, enabled its angle to be read off on a corresponding very finely divided scale on the instrument's fixed frame. Then, counting the beat of the regulator (an accurate astronomical pendulum clock), Hornsby darted to the adjacent room to lie or sit on a wheeled reclining chair beneath the eyepiece of the transit telescope pivoted on its balanced trunnions in the vertical plane, and picked up the star as it actually crossed the meridian from east to west. The transit time could be mathematically converted to an angular position equivalent to east to west celestial longitude, known as the angle of 'right ascension'. Still counting, he then darted back to the quadrant to watch the star exit across the last two wires. This method required a flawless sense of timing and an exact memory in order then to write down the two observations made in a breathless performance of less than two minutes.[16] This 'eye and ear' method of observation provided the raw data of two celestial co-ordinates for two observations of a star from one observing position on Earth for a particular night of a year. If the raw notes are carefully transcribed, and 'reduced' for publication, they become accessible for astronomers elsewhere to use to check their own observations of a particular star.

Hornsby copied out his observations with great care, but did not reduce them, so that they provided merely the data for an approximate apparent position of that star as seen in the sky. Multiple observations, on different nights, provide averaging to yield an even more accurate apparent position. The first-stage reduction of each observation required arithmetical work requiring the writing of more than 400 figures. To make a useful catalogue of the observed stars by converting apparent to true position and to a common epoch of time, the second-stage reduction had to be made, all in duplicate so as to check for errors. Several step formulae must be applied with perfect accuracy to convert the timed right ascension to an angular measurement expressed in degrees and minutes. Both the 'R.A. and Dec' angles must then be corrected for variable constants (the eccentricities in the Earth's spin and orbit detected by Bradley), refraction, known errors of the instrument (which would be left 'constant' rather than adjusted), known errors of the clock, and for temperature (noted by the assistant). The several observations of a particular star on different nights and in different years, were thus adapted by reduction through two stages. The Armagh Observatory in Ireland, with instruments very similar to the Radcliffe's, observed 5,346 stars between 1828 and 1854 and published a catalogue of them in 1859. It took three men nine years of work and 'made old men' of them.[17] John Herschel, an expert mathematician, complained that it took him half an hour to reduce each observation. It was only after publication that a selection of bright stars (and Moon, or bright planets, or the Sun) stated to be visible at very particular times from different latitudes at different times of the year, could be published as an almanac. At last the original observations then became useful to the navigator or surveyor who made his own observation of a celestial body at a time he determined as accurately as possible. With a simple table to apply the differences in time and angle, he could then estimate with some accuracy his position on the surface of the Earth.

The usual routine of the Observatory should have been for Hornsby and an assistant to work the instrument together for several hours up to midnight on every cloud-free night when the Moon was not casting too much light near their meridian. He and the assistant would then work from 9 a.m. to 2 or 3 p.m. on reductions, before resting in advance of the evening work. However, the colleges, which had neither student demand, obvious motive, nor precedent for financing the research of a professor, had silently ignored the plea two years earlier for an assistant's stipend.

On his own, Hornsby's energy and ability enabled him between 1773 and 1803 to make 80,000 transit and 20,000 zenith observations later recognized as being of excellent quality. Almost certainly for lack of an assistant to tackle the drudgery of reduction, Hornsby decided to follow the honourable tradition of astronomers bearing the responsibility to see that their predecessor's unpublished observations were at least printed so that their life-work should not be lost. Therefore during those part days that he devoted to astronomy, Hornsby chose to give priority to editing (but not reducing) Bradley's Greenwich observations for publication, and the first volume was published in 1798. In addition, Hornsby was a very diligent teacher, and lecturing took up much of his time. He was obliged to give his professorial lectures in mathematics twice a week. At the Ashmolean Museum he continued Bradley's lucrative lectures in experimental philosophy even before he was elected to the Sedleian Chair of Natural Philosophy (effectively a chair of applied mathematics) in 1782. Also at the Museum he offered lectures in astronomy, supplemented with practical classes at the Observatory. In 1783 he was appointed Radcliffe Librarian, which carried a useful stipend of £150 per year for organizing and supervising the library in the Radcliffe Camera but, perhaps due to lack of time as a result of his plural office holding, he did not perform that office diligently, and the book acquisition budget was virtually unused.[18]

With building work and expense continuing until 1795, and with his drawing a

stipend as their Librarian, Hornsby probably found it inappropriate to ask the Trustees to provide for an assistant although he could now have held no hope whatever that the University would provide an assistant's stipend. He enjoyed a free house, three stipends and the lecture income but he suffered from epilepsy and therefore employed a servant to be with him at all times to attend in case of an attack.[19] Clearly he felt that he could not personally afford an assistant as well, despite official pressure to speed the publication of Bradley's observations or to begin the reductions at a time when both the problem of navigation and the limitations of the ROG were becoming increasingly clear. Public criticism that his first volume of Bradley's observations in 1798 had taken 20 years to produce did not take account of his accumulated work, and the toll that epilepsy took of his health and energy. He made his last few observations in 1805, and now knew that he would leave a mass of unfinished work for his successor, whom he could not have imagined would be better provided for.

Hornsby died in 1810 at the age of 76, in the Observer's House. He secured his place in the history of astronomy by his remarkable role in the founding of a great observatory. However, the eventual reduction and publication by Harold Knox-Shaw in 1932 of 54,000 of his observations proved useful at that time in confirming the reference system for deducing the proper motion of stars. Hornsby's use of his beloved instruments to make many painstaking observations of Sirius then also confirmed the modern calculation for the binary nature of that star. His contribution as an observer was recognized when in 1973 a lunar crater was named after him.[20]

Hornsby's successor was Abraham Robertson (1751–1826) who exemplifies how the Savilian chairs were accessible on the basis of merit. Robertson came from humble origins in Berwick, and was a schoolmaster for a time before aspiration motivated him to arrive alone in Oxford. There he gained the patronage of Dr John Smith, the Savilian Professor of Geometry. Robertson entered Christ Church, took his BA in 1779, and then took holy orders, but preferred to succeed to Smith's chair in 1797 and make do without a clerical living. He had married in about 1790, but was widowed about ten years later, and had no children. He lectured for Professor Smith, and Robertson's numerous publications between 1792 and 1822 were all on mathematical subjects, both theoretical and practical. In 1792 his exhaustive study of the history of conic sections was instrumental in his election to the Royal Society in 1795. He did not hold plural offices but was an adviser to the government, in 1801 on the feasibility of a single span for London Bridge, in 1807 on finance, and in 1808 on a structure of loan securities. Although having no official connection with the Observatory, we may assume friendship with Hornsby, and perhaps a combination of aspiration to the latter's chair fuelled by the pressure of the Royal Society as being his motivation for undertaking the great labour of collecting and in 1805 publishing a second volume of Bradley's unreduced observations. Upon Hornsby's death in 1810 it was thus natural for the University to translate Robertson to the chair of astronomy, but the Sedleian Chair went to Stephen Rigaud (Plate 41, p. 98) who would later become Robertson's successor. Shortly afterwards the Trustees appointed Robertson, at the age of 58, to be their Observer, a post he held for 16 years.

Clearly the Trustees wanted to restore the Observatory to work, for at their meeting in June 1811 they instructed the widower Robertson to appoint an observing assistant to be accommodated with him in the Observer's House, and made an allowance of £60 for his board, lodging and washing.[21] While the name of only one of several assistants is known, the two men lived with a housekeeper tending their needs. Robertson must have found the prospect of living only on the professor's stipend insupportable because at their May 1812 meeting the Trustees augmented his salary to a total of £300, backdated to the previous summer. In return they prohibited his accepting other offices that would involve more than light attention, and charged him with faithfully keeping and supervising the recording and annual publication of observations.[22] Shortly afterwards the Trustees purchased from William Herschel at a cost of 300 guineas a new reflecting telescope of ten foot focal length, with achromatic eyepieces, all on a portable mount. From the upper observing room, this instrument could be used to observe objects in any part of the sky. Robertson and his assistant continued to extend Hornsby's observations, but the estimate of about £130 per year to publish the observations was unaffordable, and instead a copy of the observations was deposited annually in the library of the Royal Society.

Robertson's obituary records that he lived simply as a widower, helped his relatives and the poor of his home parish financially, and was a diligent teacher. In his last years he suffered considerably from various afflictions, but bore them patiently, and died in the Observer's House in December 1826, aged 75.[23] Robertson's reputation as an astronomer therefore rests entirely upon his earlier service to Bradley. For the history of the Observatory, his significance was in setting the precedent of obtaining a sufficient salary for himself as the Observer which both obviated the need for, and led directly to the Trustees prohibiting the holding of plural offices. He also established the need for an assistant to be paid by the Trustees, and he initiated the systematic recording of meteorological observations in 1816, and published those for 1816–21 as the first volume of what would become a remarkable and valuable series. These three initiatives established a basic annual budget for the Observatory.

Robertson's natural successor in 1827 was 53 year old Stephen Peter Rigaud (1774–1839). He had been a pupil of Hornsby's, a graduate and a Fellow of Exeter College, Oxford, and had deputized in giving the ailing Hornsby's natural philosophy lectures. When Robertson succeeded Hornsby in 1810, Rigaud replaced Robertson as Savilian Professor of Geometry, and Reader in Experimental Philosophy which gave him the substantial fee income from those lectures. He was already since 1805 a Fellow of the Royal Society, and since 1814 joint observer with his grandfather at the King's Observatory at Kew. Rigaud's happiness in gaining the Savilian chair and the Observer's House was destroyed the next year when his beloved young wife died, in March 1828, leaving him with seven young children to support; it was remarked that his hair turned white overnight. Apart from devotedly bringing up his family, Rigaud immersed himself in work. He made some observations himself, and supervised the assistant Angel Lockey's regular meridian observations and meteorological recording. That would have been sufficient for two men to reduce and publish, but although Rigaud was a practical astronomer both his and Robertson's observations were 'overtaken by more accurate work', and were never published.[24]

However, Rigaud's real interest in astronomy was already more scholarly and historical than practical. He was already the foremost historian of astronomy of his generation. He had accumulated a large library in the history of science, and after 1834 the Trustees helped him to supplement it annually so that it became an increasingly valuable asset of the Observatory. Rigaud's delight was to recover the lost details of biography, invention, and the process of discovery. He rediscovered Bradley's original observations and correspondence, and his first major work was an acclaimed edition of both published in 1831. He never completed an immense labour to write a life of Halley, but his transcription of nearly a thousand pages of *Letters of Scientific Men of the Seventeenth Century* recovered something of their memory, and was published after his death. Seeking solace in work, it is notable that Rigaud's books and all but one of his papers published outside Oxford were written after his arrival at the Observatory.

Of a courteous, amiable and modest nature, Rigaud was one of the founders of the Ashmolean Society in Oxford, and made many presentations and contributions to its debates on a wide range of scientific subjects. Rigaud was a long-standing member of the Board of Longitude criticized in 1822 by Francis Baily, a founder of the Astronomical Society of London, as containing learned professors who seldom attended.[25] Apart from visits to his family and the observatory at Kew, for nearly half a century Rigaud hardly ventured beyond Oxford. His absence from the learned societies and the Board arguably deprived Oxford science of an influence from which it would surely have benefited, although he served as Vice-President of the Royal Society for 1837–8. While staying with his friend the clock maker Benjamin Vulliamy in Pall Mall, Rigaud was taken ill and *The Times* reported that after eighteen hours of intense suffering he died in March 1839, aged 64, probably of a burst appendix.[26]

The entrepreneurial Hornsby had secured for Oxford the opportunity of having from 1773 to 1818 the best and, until the 1830s, one of the top four European observatories: the others were Konigsberg University Observatory established in 1818, then Cambridge from 1828 under Airy's direction, and Berlin after 1835 under Encke's direction. The first three Savilian professor-directors offered astronomy lectures and practicals at the Observatory at a time when there was very little student interest in the subject since classics rather than mathematics dominated the honours to be won at

Oxford. Quite simply, at Oxford between 1773 and 1839, despite the first stirrings of criticism of the curriculum, there was little precedent and neither academic need nor vested financial interest to motivate the academics to consider capitalizing on an institutional provision that remained in private hands. The mere existence of the Observatory could not motivate revising the mathematics syllabus as the Cambridge reformers managed to achieve between 1810 and 1817. It was Cambridge's mathematical reforms, in particular the adoption of continental analytical methods and calculus, that imparted to their observatory of 1824 a potential relevance to the university. That, and the published order of merit of the 'wranglers' in the Mathematical Tripos which now carried the university honours, gave to Cambridge a cumulative advantage for the development of astronomy throughout the nineteenth century. Meanwhile with Oxford mathematics unreformed, and even Newton not being read there, the professors had no hope of attracting more than occasional individuals to astronomy. Oxford did not make the formal academic link between analytical mathematics, physics, and astronomy until 1928. The Radcliffe's first three professor-observers achieved the publication of Bradley's raw observations but none of them published their own observations. The work of the Observatory had received little interest and no support whatsoever from the University.

By the 1830s John Bird's mural circles with small aperture telescopes had been rendered obsolete by the development in Germany of the transit circle with larger aperture. This enabled both ascension and declination measurements to be made with the single instrument, although until 1850 the English preferred to make the two observations with two instruments. In practical astronomy, Rigaud's achievement had been to persuade the Trustees to make their first re-equipment notwithstanding his own age and circumstances.[27] In 1836 they took delivery from Thomas Jones of London of a mural circle of six inch aperture and six foot focal length at a cost of £350. This affordable instrument, transitional in design between a mural quadrant and a meridian or transit circle,[28] was installed in the far room of the west wing, tested by 1838, and represented a considerable investment and forward-looking commitment by the Trustees. Regrettably Rigaud died before he could bring it into use. The Trustees purchased his scientific library of about 2,000 volumes for £330, and this became a renowned asset of the Observatory, available to members of the University.

Schism with the University

Rigaud's sudden death on 16 March 1839 triggered an extraordinary sequence of events which had the most unpredictable and far-reaching consequences both for the Radcliffe Observatory and for astronomy in the University. The Trustees had defrayed all the three professor-directors' expenses, paid the taxes on the building, since 1811 they had paid for all the expenses of an assistant, and since 1812 augmented the stipend to increase the dedication of Robertson and Rigaud to the Observatory's work, and had drawn up their terms of employment. Yet the University, without consulting the Trustees, promptly appointed to the Savilian chair George H. S. Johnson, a mathematician lacking any observatory experience. The Trustees did not consider him competent nor likely to be committed to working the new instrument they had so recently installed. It seems that Sir Robert Peel, an influential Trustee, wanted a man of science. The Trustees consulted Sir John Herschel, the most famous astronomer of the day. He recommended 35 year-old Manuel J. Johnson (1805–59) (Plate 42, p. 98), who had recently won the Gold Medal of the Royal Astronomical Society for a catalogue of southern stars made whilst serving as an officer in the East India Company; he had also recently completed a bachelors degree at Oxford. Although therefore a gentleman, and proven astronomer, he was neither an MA nor senior, so would never have been considered by the University for the vacant chair. On Herschel's recommendation, and without consulting the University, within two months in May the Trustees appointed Manuel Johnson to be their Radcliffe Observer (the first official use of that title).[29] They simultaneously withdrew the use of their Observatory from the University, which thus found itself with a new professor and no observing facilities whatever.

Hornsby's initiative of 1768 had encountered no opposition from the University because he had asked for no money. The 1839 debacle exposed the issue of ownership. Oxford University's reputation in the natural sciences was weakened, and it gradually became apparent that Oxford was less well represented than Cambridge in London's increasingly influential learned societies. Because Oxford's all-powerful colleges had no investment in the Observatory, there was no initiative to resolve matters in 1839. The ensuing 36-year hiatus until the completion of the new University of Oxford Observatory in the University Parks in 1875 broke Oxford's long tradition of theoretical and practical astronomy being taught by an active practitioner within the University, while both undergraduate and senior members had access to a major observatory. Those opportunities were now lost, and the Radcliffe would henceforth function as a private observatory dedicated to making observations for the public benefit. The price of independence was that the Trustees had to immediately begin paying their Observer the full £300 a year since he had neither professor's stipend nor lecture income. In addition they had to remunerate the Assistant, maintain the buildings (which had been achieved at a level of about £30 a year), and

bear the full cost of publication. On the other hand their Observer was now free of all teaching responsibilities.

There was one other consequence of the schism that became increasingly important as astronomy evolved during the nineteenth century. It was a science with all too few professional posts to provide careers. The virtually independent directorship of the Radcliffe Observer, bearing a reasonable stipend and free use of an excellent house amid all the facilities of a university city, became one of the most desirable posts to aspire to. As time went by, the first and second assistantships also became important posts within the patronage network. It is difficult to overestimate the influence of the coterie who ran the Royal Astronomical Society from the 1820s to about 1880, directed more or less by the long serving Astronomer Royal, George Biddel Airy, who for decades was the government's only salaried scientist. Airy held office from 1835 until his eightieth birthday in 1881 and remained on the RAS Council until 1886 during which time he could still apply an effective veto. He zealously guarded the reputation of the Society by insisting that only a practising astronomer of international reputation should be its President. By also occasionally vetoing the inappropriate award of the Society's Gold Medal he was usually able to govern the coterie of Grand Amateurs whose wealth and position, patronage of evolving telescope technology, and dominant success in the new specializations of extra-meridian astronomy, enabled them to effectively control the membership of the RAS council's offices by their invitation. Hence for decades few appointments to the key directorships and senior assistants' positions were made without Airy's direct approval. To criticize him in print or in the Society's discussions was to risk blighting all aspirations of personal advancement. Therefore, after 1839, whenever the Radcliffe Observership became vacant the new appointment was a matter of the greatest importance and interest not only to senior astronomers, but for British astronomy.[30]

Manuel J. Johnson, Observer 1839–59

The year 1839 was a real turning-point in the history of the Radcliffe Observatory, and it is important to understand the factors underlying the choices made for future work. The Cambridge University Observatory completed in 1824 was well equipped for meridian work, and by 1830 it possessed the powerful 11¾ inch Northumberland refractor. Having experienced the difficulty of reconciling meridian work with lecturing, Airy urged Professor James Challis, his successor in 1835, to avoid the drudgery of meridian work which Airy intended to dominate at the better resourced ROG. The great refractor could do important and useful astronomy that could be equally relevant to the University. Despite Airy's advice to Challis, he and his successor in 1865, John Couch Adams, both chose to stay with the mainstream meridian work. The inevitable result was that the Cambridge Observatory began to accumulate heaps of meridian observations that were second-rate by comparison to those of Bonn 1852-9 and Greenwich, and latterly to those of the great new observatories at Washington after 1877 and Pulkovo (established 1839) outside St Petersburg. They were also increasingly delayed in publication. In 1985 Dr David Dewhirst was the first to analyze Cambridge's failure, and 'the absurdity of the proposals [for founding the observatory for that purpose] and the procedure' of pursuing those observations. He showed that the lack of endowment funds to employ sufficient staff for the work was the principal characteristic which accounted for the relative failure of the university observatories in the era of meridian astronomy.[31] Apart from the quality of the work, the potential of an observatory to contribute significantly to astronomy was determined by the matching of its planned work and its resources for bringing that work to publication, the only way that it became of the slightest use. This largely explained why the Radcliffe Observatory in its first 66 years under three teaching professors failed to publish any observations of its own. The Radcliffe Observatory had no exclusive endowment, its annual running costs had to be met from the Trust's general income.

Manuel Johnson was appointed in May 1839, but necessary repairs to the house were such that he and his wife did not take up residence until 1 October, and he did not commence observations until the beginning of 1840. His working instruments were the Bird transit instrument of 1773, and the Jones mural circle of 1836. For occasional observations beyond the meridian he had the original two Dollond achromatic refractors in the tower room, but both were on portable mountings and the largest had half the aperture of the Northumberland refractor. Needing to decide upon a programme of work that would be both useful and capable of completion with the existing equipment, Johnson immediately chose to re-observe about 4,000 stars within 50 degrees of the north celestial pole observed between 1806 and 1817 by Steven Groombridge and published after his death as his *Catalogue of Circumpolar Stars etc.* (London 1838). The 30 year interval of time offered good prospects of Johnson detecting and measuring proper motions over a large area of sky. Johnson immediately had great difficulty with the Bird transit instrument, and despite a great deal of labour over three years could not compensate for its peculiarities of bending of the axis (which throws doubt on the value of Robertson's and Rigaud's observations with that instrument). He prevailed on the Trustees to have it completely rebuilt by the renowned London craftsmen Troughton and Simms.

Johnson was delighted not to be encumbered with teaching duties and academic responsibilities. The Trustees doubtless hoped that he would soon vindicate their dramatic decision. Johnson began systematic observations, and was often assisted in this by his wife. Johnson sought and was granted relatively generous resources. Right away, in 1840, he was able to engage John Lucas as Assistant on a salary of £90 per year and an allowance for his accommodation nearby. In 1847 Johnson obtained the application of the Bird Fund, revenue from a trust fund generously left by John Bird for the benefit of the Observatory, to increase John Lucas's basic stipend to £110 per year, which the Trustees then made up to £120, and in 1849 to £130. Lucas stayed with him for 15 years. Johnson also obtained the Trustees' agreement that they would publish his astronomical and meteorological Observations each year. For ten years he and Lucas together made all observations, and reduced and published them with a regularity that was without parallel.[32] From 1844 onwards they were assisted in the calculations and proof reading by Mr William Luff, a local chemist, who only after 1851 received £30 per year as a part time computer and invaluable proof-reader. Luff continued that extraordinary and almost gratuitous service until 1889, which suggests something of Johnson's charisma.[33]

The Oxford Heliometer

Meanwhile improvements in the manufacture and availability of larger glass blanks, and in the technology to mount equatorial refractors, led to new discoveries of double stars, and of more minor planets. Both attracted great public interest and international honours. This legitimization of the utility of these new fields of research beyond the meridian was consolidated when Frederich Bessel succeeded in using a new type of German refractor, a heliometer with split object glass, to make the first successful measurement of the parallax angle of a star beyond the Sun. This breakthrough in the potential to measure the distance scale of the stellar system won him the RAS Gold Medal in 1841. The delicacy of the extremely fine measurements made six months apart as the Earth reached the extremities of its orbit around the Sun which was the base-line for the measurement, and the importance and prestige of similarly discovering the distance to other stars, made it essential to have a German heliometer in England. Such research was not the business of the ROG, and certainly the universities could not afford one. The Chairman of the Radcliffe Trustees was Sir Robert Peel (a Trustee from 1828 until his death in 1850). It was he who in 1839 had arranged for the purchase of Rigaud's library and authorized the rebuilding of the Bird transit instrument in 1843. In 1841 he public spiritedly led the Trustees to order a heliometer of seven and a half inch aperture at a cost of £1,500 from Repsold's factory in Hamburg, Germany. The new tower with rotating dome to house it cost an additional £860. Installed in 1849 at a total cost of £3,500, the Radcliffe heliometer was an expensive major import of new technology into Britain and received widespread publicity so that visitors from all over the country came to admire it (Plate 47, p. 99).[34]

However, Johnson soon found that it required two men to work the heliometer and, as a direct consequence, so that reduction and publication should not suffer, in 1851 he obtained the salary for a Second Assistant (until 1879 on a scale of £70 to £100, thereafter £90 to £130). The first appointee in late 1851 was Norman Pogson (1829–91) who came from an assistantship at Mr George Bishop's private observatory in London.[35] Pogson was very ambitious, and in his own time with a borrowed instrument he discovered two new minor planets and several variable stars, which brought significant credit to the Observatory. But his family increased more rapidly than his salary, so after seven years he was compelled to move on, making a career decision that proved personally unhappy and which limited what he might have achieved. Meanwhile the splendid heliometer proved demanding to use, and problems with the dividing glass were such that craftsmen came from the manufacturers to adjust it. Painstaking and repeated observations were made of the diameters of planets when favourably placed, and of a number of selected stars, but the very specialized attention and operation that this instrument needed had to take second place to the systematic work on the meridian catalogue. Johnson had overworked and, as his health began to fail, no heliometer observations were recorded after 1855, the year in which Lucas left to take a post at Greenwich, and the very able Adolph Quirling was engaged as First Assistant.

Johnson had also extended and improved the meteorological observations. After 1847 each year's observations were not merely published, but were analyzed and discussed. By 1853 he had all observations since Rigaud's in 1828 made uniform to his own system, and published a comparison and analysis of the range of annual figures. This laborious initiative, and the introduction in 1854 of self-recording apparatus similar to that at the Kew Observatory, established the Radcliffe Observatory and its continuous sequence of observations as an international centre of excellence in meteorological recording (see Chapter 5).[36] The Trustees recognized his skills, and in 1854 at last doubled his salary to £600, which with his growing family was a necessity.

Manuel Johnson was the first Radcliffe Observer to become President of the RAS, and served for the years 1857 and 1858. A man of first-class intellect and habitual application to work, his frankness and kindness of spirit, his good humour even in argument, and in Oxford the pleasure of his company at Friday afternoon teas at the Observatory, made him a much-loved person. He and the Savilian Professor of Astronomy, William Donkin, both

believed that research was incompatible with teaching. However, after the re-equipment and the unavoidable concession of a second assistant and part-time computer, the Trustees found that the Observatory's annual expenses had nearly doubled since 1841. The expenses of running a research institution had not been foreseen. By enduring the constant fatigue and cold of observing, Johnson broke his health through overwork. He was also a heavy consumer of cigars, latterly suffered from chest pains, and died very suddenly of a stroke in March 1859 aged only 54. Only with hindsight does the value of Johnson's tenure become clear. The reputation of the Radcliffe Observatory in the nineteenth century largely rests upon his work and effective example of publishing observations when so many others outside Greenwich failed. With the help of the able John Lucas and Norman Pogson, he had completed the observations of 6,317 circumpolar stars some years before his death, the reductions were well advanced, and the catalogue was duly published. He had incorporated the meteorological work since 1828, and ensured that the work would be first class and important in future. He had persuaded the Trustees to fund, within their limited means, the staff and the publications that alone would make the Observatory internationally reputable. He sacrificed his own health to that end.

Johnson's achievements enhanced the status and desirability of the Radcliffe Observership as a post within the profession. Nevertheless the Trustees were very concerned by the level of annual expense, and enquired in the University as to whether the offices could again be combined in order to save the Observer's salary. Professor Donkin, whose health was not robust, objected strongly.[37] His veto decided the issue but clearly the new Observer would have to practise the strictest economy. The candidates to succeed Johnson illustrate the small pool of professional talent available; this made apparent for the first time the disadvantage of Oxford University in failing to produce mathematicians who would naturally seek the directorship and challenge Cambridge graduates to the Oxford post. Despite the fixed salary and small annual budget, the post was independent, prestigious and therefore of great interest. This election and that of 1878 also illuminate the way in which Airy deployed his patronage.

In 1859 the applicants for the Observership were Robert Main (1808–78) (Plate 43, p. 98), sixth wrangler and Airy's First Assistant for 23 years, and current President of the RAS, aged 41; Richard Carrington aged 33, thirty-sixth wrangler and an MA, current Secretary of the RAS, and the Society's 1859 Gold Medal winner; and Norman Pogson aged 31, the former assistant to Manuel Johnson, discoverer of minor planets and of variable stars and currently director of a well known private observatory, who enjoyed some of Airy's favour. A fifteen month hiatus ensued whilst the Trustees sought advice on future work. The post was then re-advertised at £500. To Carrington's fury, without calling any candidate for interview to hear their views, the Trustees accepted Airy's three-page recommendation and appointed Robert Main.[38] Airy sympathized with Pogson sufficiently to explain honestly:

> Mr Main's claims on me ... are like those of a son on the head of the family. ... This almost prevents me from saying a word in favour of any other person.[39]

Carrington, like Johnson in 1839, had both the Oxbridge 'polish' considered necessary for the post, and recent and acclaimed research. He also knew that he had made himself contentious by criticizing Airy's work in Council. The election showed that without Airy's recommendation for this post, or the directorship of the Cambridge Observatory which became available in 1861, ability alone would not be sufficient.

Robert Main, Observer 1860–78

Following Manuel Johnson's death in March 1859, the routine meridian work was continued by the able Quirling alone (he died in 1869). The Trustees were now concerned that with the necessity to pay the Observer £500 per year (to bear comparison with the ROG scale), and the assistants £120 and £80 respectively, the annual expense of the Observatory would be £1,200. Soon there would also be the expense of publishing Johnson's star catalogue. The Trustees turned to the University's Dr Henry Acland to seek advice within the astronomy community as to policy for their Observatory. The unanimous advice was to drop the meridian work and to keep the heliometer going.[40] Sir John Herschel had recommended 'the intrinsic importance' of parallax work which required 'a very long and persevering series of observations'.[41] Airy advised that determining the parallax of one star 'would well repay the labours of an observatory through many years'.[42]

However, this advice came from astronomers with no personal experience of the heliometer, and illustrates the gulf between laudable aspirations for the Radcliffe to win international renown in astronomy, and what the Observatory could actually achieve on a day-to-day basis. Using two people to work the heliometer overstretched the resources of the Observatory, and the divided object glass proved very difficult to adjust so that an astronomer lost the confidence to commit to the very complex parallax observations. It was logical instead to test the instrument by measuring the diameters of planets at favourable oppositions (when in some years their orbits brought them into positions high in the sky opposite to the Sun), or the separation of double stars, although for that latter work the instrument's aperture was uncompetitively small. Although all astronomers recognized that meridian work was 'soul wearying',[43] there are good reasons why the Radcliffe and other observatories could not embrace equatorial work. Refractor technology was expensive, and high risk – as the heliometer had proven. A large equatorial is harder to work than a meridian instrument, requires more expertise, and takes a longer time to make observations.[44] Not least, it often requires the observer to stay up longer at night waiting for his objects. That had much to do with the breakdown in health of a number of first-class observers. Richard Sheepshanks, doyen of the RAS, harangued Challis at Cambridge that 'the labour of an equatorial ... is too great to pay'.[45] Challis also found that for the type of observation made, utility meant that very prompt publication was essential, and 'The reduction entails so much calculation [that it] can only be affected by command of sufficient computers'.[46] Compared to this more glamorous but arduous observing beyond the meridian with its known health risks, meridian work was a safe option – respectable, potentially useful, and affordable.

More than a year after Johnson's death, the Trustees in the summer of 1860 appointed Robert Main, aged 52, to be their Observer, and he and his wife Mary and their three sons, without having been able to take any holiday after completing his duties at Greenwich, moved into the Observer's House at Oxford on 1 October 1860. From Greenwich he re-engaged John Lucas as Second Assistant. Main knew full-well the significance of Airy's 1851 re-equipment of the ROG with a state-of-the-art transit circle with eight inch aperture constructed to Airy's specification on the German model. It had a battery-powered chronograph attached in order to minimize the observer's personal error of logging the exact time of the star crossing the wires. At a stroke, by making both observations of a star's position with one instrument of such power so solidly mounted, eliminating the eye-and-ear method, and being able to publish the observations annually, all other British

meridian instruments were rendered obsolete. Therefore Main knew that the work he had to undertake could not be comparable. The extent of his compromise is apparent in that he was only able to persuade the Trustees to invest £420 in the five inch Carrington Transit Circle, with a further grant of £180 to remove and install it in 1861. This instrument had been made in 1854 for Richard Carrington, and enabled him to win his RAS medal (Plate 49, p. 100). However, although it represented an advance in type and size for the Observatory and although Main improved it by adding four new micrometers to improve the accuracy of observations taken, the Carrington Circle was already second class, and there were neither the funds to purchase nor labour available to maintain the complicated battery apparatus to enable the time of observations to be self-recording. Therefore Main and his assistants' work from 1862 to 1878, using the old 'eye and ear' method, was destined to make no fundamental contribution. After his death, Stone did not see it to press, and it was only published in Germany in 1910 as The Third Radcliffe Catalogue, 5,839 stars for epoc 1910. Meanwhile Main chose to work the heliometer, concentrating on planetary diameters, some stellar parallax observations, double stars and the occasional comets and transits. Main had been urged by Carrington to continue sun spot observations. A photograph, labelled as 1861 but from the known date of installation of a clock in its run-off cover perhaps 1873, illustrates Main's affordable initiative with 'the 7 inch Telescope' about which little is known (Plate 48, p. 99). Ivor Guest recorded that the Duke of Wellington had purchased from James South a 7.25 inch Cauchoix object glass (at that time a significant size) and in 1834 gave it to the University of Oxford, who in turn gave it to the Observatory since the Trustees would not accept a loan. There is no record of Rigaud's using it, and it is likely that Johnson had it mounted as a refractor to supersede the power of the old Dollond telescopes. Superseded in turn by the Heliometer in 1849, Main found the refractor damaged and in disrepair, and in 1861 had it thoroughly repaired and thereafter used for solar observations. The fate of this instrument is not known.

Following Quirling's death in 1869, in 1870 Main's First Assistant was John Lucas, and he needed a Second Assistant. Airy was more direct than with the gentlemen applicants for the Radcliffe Observership. He recommended George Keating, a ROG boy computer on £5.5s. a month (£63 per annum), for the £100 post. He simply instructed Keating: 'You will write to Main, accepting the post'.[47] Main's supervision of the meridian work should be seen within the context of his hopes to master the heliometer. As recently as 1858 he had received the RAS Gold Medal for work including a twelve year study of planetary diameters. He was ideally suited to do useful work with the heliometer, if it could be made completely reliable. He did indeed work to master the instrument, and during the unusually near approach of Mars in 1862 attempted to measure the ellipticity of that planet. Up until 1875 he regularly used the heliometer to measure the separation and relative positions of double stars (which he reduced himself and published, but did not catalogue), and the diameters of planets, but perhaps lingering doubts as to the long-term adjustment of the object glass dissuaded him from undertaking the commitment to attempting stellar parallaxes. Main completed publication of Manuel Johnson's work as *The First Radcliffe Catalogue*, and then in 1870 published the observations of 1854–61 as *The Second Radcliffe Catalogue* of 2,386 stars. He served on the RAS Council for 39 years, and was very active there until his removal to Oxford. Thereafter he attended when important matters were to be discussed and always attended the December meeting which decided the award of the Society's Medal.

Given his limited opportunities for research at Oxford, it is clear that Main would have thrived in the University. He read fluently in nine languages beside Greek and Latin. He had already translated F. Brünnow's *Spherical Astronomy* from the German. In 1863 Main of his own volition wrote an astronomy textbook for university students, and in 1867 after lecturing for the Savilian Professor William Donkin who was ill, reported to the Trustees that he had enjoyed 'that friendly and intimate connexion with the university which is evidently most desirable' and would make the work of his observatory better known.[48] Thus he might well have been considered when the chair became vacant upon Donkin's death in 1870 but all parties ignored the rare opportunity and the moment passed. Main's health broke suddenly and after a short illness he died on 9 May 1878 in the Observer's House, aged 70.[49] John Lucas's health was failing and Frederic Bellamy the Second Assistant died only two days after Main.

The new University Observatory of 1875

More than 30 years after the schism between the Trustees and University, the history of the Radcliffe Observatory again began to intersect with developments in the University's astronomy. This time initiatives by University men would contribute to great difficulties for Main's successor.

Once again the initiative to advance astronomy within the University was taken by a professor who was determined to light the flame of astronomy in the University but he could not have done so without dry tinder. The latter was available because his appointment in 1870 coincided with the threat posed to the University by an imminent Royal Commission (the Devonshire Commission of 1872) that would inevitably criticize the University's lack of investment in the natural sciences.

Following Professor Donkin's death in 1869, there is no evidence that the University even sounded Main or approached the Trustees to discuss re-merging the two offices. Instead, and without delay, in 1870 they appointed to the Savilian chair the 62 year-old Reverend Charles Pritchard (1808–93), who had made a reputation as a teacher of natural science in his own London school. Pritchard had served the RAS well as Secretary 1862-6 and then was elected President 1866–8, somewhat to his own surprise since he had no great experience as an observer. Pritchard was delighted to have been appointed to the Savilian Chair through the influence of his RAS friends but he soon found the small teaching observatory behind the University Museum totally inadequate. One of his colleagues there was the Keeper of the Museum and the Professor of Geology, John Phillips, who was a keen astronomer. Phillips stimulated, helped plan, and then guided through committees and Convocation an application by Pritchard in February 1873 to build a proper teaching observatory with a 12 inch refractor which was available for early delivery from Howard Grubb of Dublin.

The astronomical world was astonished when in March (with the Commission gathering evidence) the University granted the £2,500 request. For good reasons of his own, Pritchard's friend Warren De La Rue in June offered his famed 13 inch photographic reflector provided that it be properly housed. By November the university had thus been manipulated into granting an additional £1,500 to double the size of the observatory, and to locate it on a better site in the University Parks. The new University of Oxford Observatory was completed there in 1875. Pritchard wisely chose not to involve himself with meridian work. Instead the Grubb 12 inch refractor would serve both for some research and for advanced teaching. He had a set of smaller instruments for teaching practical astronomy classes. Most important, De La Rue paid for a Second Assistant and for all the incidental expenses of photography and

research so that Pritchard could work without requesting the University for additional money.[50]

The result of these developments was that whereas the astronomical work of the Radcliffe Observatory since 1861 remained increasingly inconsequential because it had no first class instrument, suddenly in 1875 a completely new observatory had been established only half a mile away. This appeared clearly to meet the University's current needs, and therefore made a merging of the offices once again unlikely. However, a more careful appraisal illuminates the actual experience of the Radcliffe Observatory as it declined for the rest of the century. The new University Observatory certainly looked splendid in its setting in the Parks, potent and modern. Pritchard proudly proclaimed in *The Times* of 3 January 1875 that: 'The University has led in England for the first foundation of an observatory for astronomical physics.' He was thus committed to research in that new branch of astronomy however elementary his mathematical lectures and practical classes would have to remain. His observatory was actually a hybrid. Pritchard was already approaching 68 years of age, and in fact never himself observed at Oxford. De La Rue's photographic reflector was 26 years old, and used a speculum metal mirror, not modern silvered glass. Pritchard's friend John Gassiot gave him a magnificent Browning eight prism laboratory spectroscope (and was duly honoured with an honorary doctorate).

However, Pritchard had neither a laboratory such as Dr Herman Vogel included at the new Potsdam Astrophysical Observatory in 1876, or Lord Lindsay soon built at his private Dun Echt Observatory. Pritchard could not afford the ancillary instruments, nor expect to obtain experienced staff to operate them, and there is no evidence that the magnificent spectroscope was ever used. The University had granted a very modest £200 per year to include both the assistant's stipend and all other expenses. However, in contrast to Main's situation at the Radcliffe Observatory, the crucial difference was immediately apparent that benefactors such as De La Rue and Gassiot were attracted to universities, and not to private institutions. By paying for the vitally necessary second assistant and for other research expenses, De La Rue lubricated Pritchard's work at the Observatory for 15 years, enabling him to concentrate on two medal-winning research projects, in photometry and in photographic parallax.

Meanwhile, only three years after Pritchard began working the new observatory, Main's death on 9 May 1878 precipitated another election that proved that Airy's patronage remained a decisive influence upon the role and work of the Radcliffe Observatory. That there were only four applicants again reflects how small the profession still was. The first was Airy's Chief Assistant W. H. M. Christie aged 33, who sought independence. The second was Edward Stone (1831–97) (Plate 44, p. 98) aged 47, former fifth wrangler and then First Assistant at the ROG, and currently Royal Astronomer at the government's Cape of Good Hope Observatory, which pres-tigious post was in Airy's gift. The third was David Gill aged 34, director of the important private Dun Echt Observatory. Once again there was Norman Pogson, now aged 49 and Astronomer in Madras by Airy's recommendation, who was desperate to return home. Airy provided the Trustees with a resumé of each candidate. He knew that he himself wanted to retire in 1881, and intended to nominate Christie as the internal candidate to succeed; to the Trustees he merely declared him 'fully competent'. He said Gill was 'well known' and 'fully acquainted with the heliometer'. Airy attested to Pogson's 'ability and gentlemanly conduct', and to his discovery of minor planets. Stone was given two pages of high praise.[51] The ROG files show that Charles Pritchard, the caretaking

director of the Radcliffe Observatory after Main's death, and Airy's man in the RAS Council, shamelessly managed the election by suppressing Gill's foreign testimonials and Pogson's own statement and, then by backing Airy's preference.[52] Stone was appointed; when he had to be replaced at the Cape, Airy's recommendation was again crucial: Gill and Christie competed for the post, and Airy ensured that Gill was appointed.

Edward Stone, Observer 1879–97

Stone had married in 1866, and his son and three daughters moved in to the Observer's House with their parents in the summer of 1879, but on arrival in Oxford his situation was unenviable. He was shocked by the state of the Observatory and its 30 year old instruments. He asked the Trustees for the necessary higher salaries to recruit better qualified assistants, and for a new transit circle and clock that would together cost about £2,500, but the Trustees felt unable to provide this. Lucas had just been pensioned leaving one assistant, young H. E. Bellamy, who had only meteorological experience. In October Stone engaged Arthur Bowden (but had to dismiss him in 1880). He then engaged William H. Robinson in 1879, and in 1880 engaged Walter Wickham, at last finding two reliable assistants of his own.

Stone himself was a diligent but not remarkable Observer. His intellectual interest was in refining astronomical constants and tables. In 1869 he had been awarded the RAS Gold Medal for his re-discussion of the Venus Transit of 1769. His principal interest was to determine the Solar parallax, i.e. to find the accurate distance to the Sun, but his values proved consistently too high. In 1870, anxious to escape from Greenwich, he had sought Airy's approval to be appointed Astronomer at the Cape. He returned with the *Cape Catalogue of 12,400 southern stars for epoch 1880*, and in the following decade published *The Radcliffe Catalogue of 1890 for 6,424 southern stars* (1894) that he had observed while at the Cape. Upon his earlier work on constants and upon these two catalogues his reputation rests, because from 1883 until his death in 1897 he was obsessed with disputing the basis of Solar and Lunar tables.

Stone inherited a barely adequate annual budget, and no prospect of major instrument renewal. When the transit could not be afforded he sought approval to buy a second-hand reflector in order to undertake spectroscopy, but the reality was that, because the Trust had limited revenues while at the same time the cost of new technology had increased, from 1860 until 1906 the Radcliffe Observatory had to busy itself making and publishing second-quality meridian observations.

The Trustees were at last again inclined to see if co-operation could be arranged with Pritchard. Stone disliked Pritchard because he had publicly commented on the rundown state of the Radcliffe Observatory, but in the circumstances thought that Pritchard might not last long, and that the Radcliffe Observatory should then be used as originally intended for the University. With the Devonshire Committee still sitting, Lord Selborne, Chairman of the Trustees, thought that they might mediate. Selborne soon realized that by building their new observatory, the University had complicated the equation with new interests. The offices belatedly separated by statute in 1858 could now only be merged by statute, and the stakes were higher. New posts had been created, and in those days the wishes of senior unpensioned incumbents were usually respected. The Trustees wished to honour their foundation's traditional intimate links to Oxford and its University, while maintaining their prestigious Observatory and its ability to do reputable work even though it was severed from the University. This aspiration was constantly in tension with their limited annual income; with hindsight it is clear that 1875 to 1902 was

the one period when the Radcliffe Observatory was worse equipped and under more financial strain than the University Observatory, so that debate might have been constructive. The problem, however, was very complex. Pritchard had told the Commissioners in 1877 that the professor had no time to be Radcliffe Observer as well. The participants each aged quicker than possibilities could be meaningfully explored.

Meanwhile the international interest and award of honours reflected that astronomy was entering the era of photography and then of astrophysics. Stone's observatory was divorced from the university, and lacked the usual and crucial board of visitors who could be lobbied to influence the Trustees. The issue of ownership would become increasingly important as a number of major benefactions of instruments and money flowed to the Cambridge Observatory to enhance its evolution into specialization in astrophysics. The Radcliffe Observatory was stuck with limited aims and potential, unable to make a mark. Far from being inclined to co-operate with the University, Stone, who served as President of the RAS for 1882–4, had to watch Pritchard, who was no observer, win two RAS gold medals for the new University Observatory and cut a figure as Airy's man in the RAS council.

From 31 August until 10 December 1885 Stone used the heliometer to make a series of excellent observations of a new nova (now known to have been a supernova) in the Andromeda nebula (now known to be a galaxy), but the instrument's aperture was small. Stone persuaded J. Gurney Barclay, an amateur he would have met regularly at the RAS, to donate his 10 inch Cooke refractor (the Barclay Refractor, a splendid instrument which had probably cost c.£1,200 in 1862) provided that it was mounted and used. It was installed in March 1887 first under a wooden run-off observatory in the Lower Field, until in 1907 it was remounted in the heliometer tower (Plates 51 and 52, p. 101). For the next decade Stone used it regularly to observe the Andromeda nebula, and the instrument gave the Observatory better capability for observing transits, comets, novae, and minor planets.

Stone was unfortunate in having taken up direction of England's most prestigious private observatory just as a new technology presented opportunities that could not then be met. After about 1873 dry-plate photography gave a new impetus and potential to work in 'astronomical physics' – research into the physical constitution and evolution of celestial bodies. This might involve planetary or satellite surfaces, the atmosphere of the Sun or planets, or research to discover the nature and dynamics of the nebulae. Photography, with its timed exposures to gather ever-fainter detail or spectra on to plates of constantly improving reliability, eliminated the personal factors of eye, pencil, and visual registration and interpretation. As the new science of 'astrophysics' became established, it drove the specialization and professionalization of research. There were two fundamental effects upon astronomy during the four decades from 1873 to the outbreak of war in 1914. First, independent research gradually shifted from the independent Grand Amateurs to the universities, to whom they donated a number of fine instruments. Second, the practitioners of astronomy increasingly needed a training in mathematics and physics or chemistry. This required a longer time than the three year bachelor's degree, and thus by the last decade of the century the 'advanced' or 'research student' sought opportunities to work in university observatories or laboratories. These trends, and the potential for the first time to attract first class physics students to study astrophysical problems within applied mathematics, began to transform university astronomy. An informal school of astrophysics evolved at Cambridge in the 1890s, another more formally at Oxford after 1934. For the

twentieth century, no professional astronomer could any longer be a mere observer, nor a mere observer be a professional.

Meanwhile, Stone's assistants laboured with the Carrington Circle operated with the old eye and ear method. With the site increasingly hampered by smoke and light pollution as the city spread north, the Observatory could not compete with the mountain sites beginning to be used by the Americans. The advantages of independence relished by Johnson, and doubted by Main, had now become an isolating disadvantage. The problems were not unique but the Radcliffe lacked both the potential support that a professor might muster from his faculty of natural science colleagues, and a board of visitors composed of other professional astronomers who might have supported the Observer in prevailing upon the Trustees more effectively.

Stone was highly respected within the RAS, and served as President 1882-4. His sudden death at the Observatory in 1897 at the age of only 66, from pneumonia brought on after a boating accident, once again throws light upon how filling a leading post in British astronomy lagged the pace of technical innovation that was now driving international competition.

Unlike chemistry or physics, astronomy had no links to industry. When Airy retired at the age of 80 in 1881, his successor as Astronomer Royal was his Chief Assistant, William Mahoney Christie, age 36. Christie has been credited with having a broader vision than Airy's as to how astronomy should be evolving, and instead of enjoying or using patronage he preferred to serve the RAS Council. This strengthened that body by giving equal voice to the wealthy expert amateurs who were important practitioners of extra-meridian work as well as patrons of technical innovation, to the photographic and solar specialists, and to Christie's very able younger colleagues Herbert Hall Turner and Frank Dyson. However, until 1924 the

Radcliffe Trustees did not feel the need to have a professional astronomer on their board to help guide their important institution. Once again, in 1897, the few candidates for the Observership illustrate two issues: the continued lack of Oxford mathematicians attracted to astronomy in the nineteenth century, and Oxford's failure to generate any alternative to the Cambridge–Greenwich axis which was still the backbone of the networks and committees that ran the RAS, the Royal Society and the British Association for the Advancement of Science.

There had been three candidates in 1860, four in 1878, and now there were six in 1897. Airy's successor Christie showed no interest in the election and failed to give timely references to some candidates. This lapse became particularly significant because his silence left the Trustees to make their own decision (without, it may be noted, referring to Professor H. H. Turner who had moved from the Chief Assistantship at Greenwich to succeed Pritchard at Oxford in 1894). The Trustees appointed Arthur A. Rambaut (1859-1923) (Plate 45, p. 98), sometime Gold Medallist in Mathematics and Mathematical Physics at Trinity College, Dublin, Assistant and then for five years Andrews Professor and Director of Trinity's Dunsink Observatory. In 1891 his observations had contributed to a new method for calculating the orbit of spectroscopic binary stars, and he noted a method by which accurate parallax data could be derived for visual binary stars. Nevertheless, Turner, who was acutely aware of the international advances, and of the need for Britain to invest in astrophysics, saw the appointment as a wasted opportunity, and, despite knowing that Christie was not at all in good health, chided him with a letter from Oxford:

> My dear Christie, While you have been inactive they have elected Rambaut. Yours, H. H. Turner.[53]

This proved to be a rather ungenerous assessment.

Arthur A. Rambaut, Observer 1897–1924

At the age of 38, Rambaut moved into the Observer's House with his wife and three young sons. The plight of the Radcliffe Observatory was known to astronomers. Upon taking office in 1897 Rambaut made good the astronomer's debt of honour. He supervised the use of the Carrington Circle to complete in 1906 the observations for Stone's last catalogue. Rambaut also made an effort to publish the observations of the first three Observers, but the relatively high cost mentioned in his public appeal unfortunately brought him into a conflict with his neighbour and contemporary, Professor Turner, who was a leading influence in the RAS. Unwisely for both men, a difference that might have been privately resolved was aired in the RAS's unofficial journal *The Observatory* (to which Turner was a regular contributor) and thus left a bitter residue of non-communication between them which would later do Turner no good.

Nevertheless, beyond this Rambaut must have enjoyed the full confidence of the Trustees, and he surely had considerable powers of persuasion. The obsolescence of the instruments and even of the fabric of the buildings could no longer be ignored. The choice was increasingly between immediate major expenditure and foreseeable closure. The Trustees deserve all credit for a bold decision, and now the fortunes of the proximate Oxford observatories began to reverse. Between 1930 and 1935 the consequences would prove cataclysmic for both.

Almost immediately upon taking office in 1897 Rambaut persuaded the Trustees to completely refurbish their observatory and to re-equip it with a magnificent 24 inch/18 inch photographic/visual double refractor by Grubb of Dublin (Plate 50, p. 100). This instrument required a new tower fitted with a rising floor. Installed in 1903 at a total cost of £10,000, the Double Equatorial was the third largest refractor in Britain, and the twin of the Victoria Telescope at the Cape Observatory. Of the large refractors made by Howard Grubb between 1882 and 1923, the Oxford telescope is arguably the best.[54] People came from afar to look at it in wonder, but within two months of being mounted in April both objective glasses had to be dismounted to remove moisture that had penetrated between the lenses. It soon became apparent that in Oxford the power of the instrument exceeded the number of good nights of weather conditions during which it could be used to full effect.

In 1906 Rambaut completed the last meridian observations, and beyond finishing reduction and publication he dropped meridian work. Under Turner's direction since 1894 the University Observatory was becoming increasingly devoted to the *Carte du Ciel*, an international co-operation of 18 observatories using relatively wide-field photography to contribute to all-sky photographic charts and catalogue. Rambaut decided to commit his new telescope to a different international programme, the photographing of Kapteyn Areas (named after the Dutch astronomer who had proposed the scheme). This project complemented two all-sky photographic mapping projects by photographing selected small areas of the sky at two epochs about 25 years apart and with long exposures in order to reveal the proper motion of nearer stars. It was expected that this would provide valuable new data on the dynamics of the nearer part of our star system (or galaxy as it became known in the 1920s). Rambaut also planned to attempt to determine some stellar distances by measuring photographic parallax. The future reputation of the Radcliffe Observatory was thus committed to photographic work utilizing the superb Double Refractor. Rambaut's obituarist W. M. H. Greaves noted that whilst

the latter work required and was given great patience, enthusiasm, and thoroughness, the parallax work was undertaken before it became clear that large systematic errors would result from the photographic spread of light unless the bright parallax stars were dimmed by use of an occulting shutter.

Rambaut was of a cheerful disposition, charming and popular. He pursued his work diligently, and enjoyed his family life in Oxford. However several attempts failed to secure a salary increase, and the shortage of assistants due to the war overworked him. By 1922 his health was failing, he missed the Trustees' annual meeting, and after more than a year's illness he died in October 1923 at the age of 64.

The problems of the Proximate Observatories, 1900–30

The experience of the first three directors of the Radcliffe Observatory exemplify the difficulties of mathematician astronomers working an observatory purportedly for the public good because the university in which they professed, taught and drew a salary, had neither interest in nor use for their research work. A century later, in 1875, with the University being compelled to respond to the new science of astronomical physics, the experience of the Radcliffe Observers can only be understood within the context of the relationship to the University's observatory and internal politics.

Herbert Hall Turner (1861–1930), Chief Assistant at the ROG, succeeded Pritchard in 1894 as Savilian Professor and Director of the University Observatory. It is rare that one observatory blights the work of another, but the University was heading into straightened circumstances, towards its first ever public appeal in 1907 for financial assistance from the government. Against that financial background, as the obsolescence of the University Observatory became more apparent the spectacular re-equipment of the Radcliffe Observatory brought the relationship between the Trust and the University into increasingly sharp focus.

Pritchard had directed work that won two gold medals, and thereby achieved instrument renewal by a benefactor supplying the only significant new instrument obtained between 1875 and 1938. Pritchard's research and the stipend of his Second Assistant had been met by his benefactor Warren de La Rue. In 1887 De La Rue additionally offered £600, and eventually paid £1,000 for a 13 inch photographic astrograph telescope, which in 1888 was mounted coaxially with the 12 inch Grubb refractor. He did so on condition that the University increase Pritchard's annual budget to £600 per year. This enabled Pritchard in 1887 to commit to a part of the international *Carte du Ciel* photographic map and catalogue. Crucially, because of De La Rue's generosity Pritchard had made no disagreeable demands upon the University for money. For that reason by the time of his death in 1893 the proximity of the now obsolete Radcliffe Observatory was not problematic to the University. However, by the end of the next decade the operating conditions for the two observatories were completely reversed.

In 1894 Professor Turner was 33 years old. As a highly competent Chief Assistant at the ROG he had been involved from the beginning in the planning and technical challenges of the *Carte du Ciel* and its catalogue. He came to the unendowed Oxford University Observatory committed to photographic zones that would yield about 400,000 images of 250,000 stars, each requiring reduction. Turner met that challenge by devising a new measuring instrument and method of reduction direct from the plates that would make it possible to employ semi-skilled labour to make the approximately one million measurements of co-ordinates, and use less than 40 numbers for each. There would then be the onerous five-year

work of preparation and proof-reading for publication.

With no new instruments after 1888, the Observatory inevitably declined. Turner's annual budget was inadequate; there were no funds for research (nor after 1914 for a regular second assistant). Turner was an internationalist, determined to complete the Oxford zones of the Catalogue, and then to see that other observatories completed theirs in order to validate the whole scheme. With the photography completed in 1904, himself and his assistants engaged on reduction for publication, and his own university extension lecturing being additional to his teaching commitment, in 1906 for the third time Turner petitioned for a house because he found the stress of term life so great. To maximize his own effectiveness at work, he pleaded for his college to be allowed to build a house for him beside the Observatory. This had been snubbed in 1896 and 1901. It seems that Turner believed that because there would be no cost to the University, he could disregard the larger financial problems. In contrast, for promoters of the University's appeal to government, any appearance of waste or duplication had to be avoided. The issue was sensitive because science professors had previously pleaded for and won investment, but had then failed to build departments relevant to students.[55] Turner grasped at the opportunity to try for a decision at the meeting of Congregation (all MAs of the University) scheduled for 12 March 1907. However, although in 1901 the argument of the duplication of resources as regards the proximate Radcliffe Observatory had been brought against him, he had done nothing to win over opponents. His timing was awful, since Convocation was preoccupied with the election of a new Chancellor on 14 March. In particular, he had not sought to persuade William R. Anson (1843–1914), Warden of All Souls, MP for Oxford University, a member of Hebdomadal Council until 1905, and a

Radcliffe Trustee, who 'had a commanding position in university affairs … holding strong opinions himself'.[56]

Turner's attempt became a *cause célèbre* because it involved private correspondence behind his back between university members and some Trustees, the usual pamphlet war in Congregation, then a bitter exchange in *The Times*. In short, Rambaut was approached by university members regarding possible amalgamation. He had fallen out with Turner after the sharp dispute in the journal *Observatory* about the cost Rambaut proposed for publishing Hornsby's observations. Rambaut's report reached Anson. Only when Anson saw Turner's proposal in 1907 did he check that there was no legal impediment to amalgamation. Motivated by the need to publicly demonstrate financial prudence publicly, he armed an opposition to the maintenance of more than a telescope for teaching purposes. Turner lost by 155 votes to 55. Too late, Turner warmed to the fray and accused Anson of duplicity,[57] then stated his case in *The Times*, accusing Oxford of disliking observation and experiment.[58] Anson replied that Turner had not furnished an argument 'for the maintenance in Oxford of two fully equipped observatories little more than half a mile apart'.[59] Anson conceded a meeting between the Trustees and Hebdomadal Council for 24 May, and Turner at last produced a five page pamphlet showing with great clarity the totally different work of the two observatories, that there was no duplication, and that both did good work.[60] In fairness to Anson, the onus was not upon him to seek the detail of Turner's case unless he believed that the Trustees had a real need to pursue amalgamation, which after 1902 was not the case. Nevertheless, Anson, as a Trustee well aware of the desirability of saving a senior salary, tabled a proposal that next time the Radcliffe Observership was vacant it should be taken *ex officio* by the Professor, and implied that the University Observatory should be allowed to run down.[61]

The wrangling of 1907 further marginalized the University Observatory with its lack of students, often the lack of a graduate second assistant, and frustrated any hope of obtaining any increase in the annual grant. Turner was convinced that the existence of the refurbished Radcliffe Observatory had crippled his work since 1901. In practice that was true but the *casus belli* only existed because his Observatory was an institution with an ill-defined role that could demonstrate little relevance to the University's teaching and examined curriculum at a time when financial pressures had brought the University, its finances and attitudes, under intense public scrutiny.

The relevance of Turner's plight is that despite his intensely felt suspicions and resentments of the Trustees, his determination to safeguard the larger interests of British astronomy led him to ally himself wholeheartedly with the next Radcliffe Observer. Indeed, in 1929 Turner negotiated an entirely new co-operation between the Radcliffe and University observatories which, ironically, was only thwarted when he became a victim of vicious politics within his own Faculty. This last phase of the troubled relationship consequent upon the proximate observatories lasted from the death of Rambaut in October 1923 to the final resolution in July 1934 of a legal action which the University took against the Trustees. That case did not deflect the Trust from its new plan for relocating their Observatory in South Africa, but it did profoundly affect the future of their Observatory once it had relocated.[62]

Harold Knox-Shaw, Observer 1924–50

Following Rambaut's death in October 1923, the Trustees again considered amalgamation in order to reduce their annual commitment. In November Lord Cottesloe sought the Astronomer Royal Sir Frank Dyson's opinion, who suggested appointing a deputy acceptable to Turner who would take charge of the

Radcliffe Observatory, and might succeed to the Savilian chair in due course. He even suggested Harold Knox-Shaw (1885–1970) (Plate 46, p. 98) sixth wrangler and currently Director of the Helawan Observatory in Egypt. The University had also formed a committee to consider the possibility of amalgamation. This committee comprised Turner, Professor F. A. Lindemann, and J. L. E. Dreyer (former director of Armagh Observatory, 1916 RAS Gold Medallist, President RAS 1923-4), and in December the Trustees met them. Lindemann, director of the Clarendon physics laboratory, was heard first, and clearly had his own agenda which specifically needed use of the Double Refractor. Perhaps fearing a loss of autonomy to Lindemann, and mindful of Dyson's and Turner's reluctance to suppress a post, the Trustees decided to maintain their independence, and appointed Knox-Shaw. A bachelor for some years to come, he commenced work in Oxford in August 1924.

Knox-Shaw's first success was in obtaining a Royal Society grant for the computation and publication (in 1932) of Hornsby's observations from 1774–98. As regards the observing programme, Rambaut had taken the first epoch plates of stars to the fourteenth magnitude in the 115 northern Kapteyn Selected Areas. Knox-Shaw set himself to the much larger task of obtaining the long exposure second epoch plates, and to measure both sets of plates in order to detect any proper motions among about 32,000 stars during the intervening period. *The Radcliffe Catalogue of Proper Motions* was duly published in 1934.[63]

However, compared to the conditions he was used to in Egypt, Knox-Shaw soon found that less than 30 nights a year at Oxford were of excellent atmospheric conditions for the photography, and in 1928 he was seeking support to move the Observatory to a fine-weather site. In 1929 he proposed and costed a plan to move the Double Equatorial and a new reflector of 36 inch aperture to South Africa. The Radcliffe Infirmary, the city's hospital adjacent to the Observatory, was desperate to expand, and the only possibility was on to the nine acre Observatory site. In November 1929 Lord Nuffield very generously offered to pay the Trustees £100,000 for the site, a sum amply sufficient to build a new observatory on a hill above Oxford, or abroad. Site testing on a plateau near Pretoria, South Africa, was put in hand.

Meanwhile, Knox-Shaw was Secretary of the RAS from 1926–30 (and President 1931-2), and Professor Turner was a very regular attendee of the Society, and of its dining club which met before the monthly meetings; the two Oxford astronomers had much opportunity to discuss possibilities. The Nuffield purchase represented the only conceivable possibility for Britain to have a fine weather and high altitude site in the southern hemisphere. It is impossible to overstate the importance of this plan for British astronomy. For lack of access by university astronomers to such a site Britain had lost its international lead in observational astronomy to America. At the January meeting of the Visitors to the University Observatory, Knox-Shaw described his plans, and Turner expressed wholehearted support not least in the interests of Oxford astronomy. He outlined a detailed plan of co-operation for the University Observatory to use South African observations, for Turner's observatory to absorb the Radcliffe's surplus assistants at the Trustees' expense to work on Radcliffe data under Turner's supervision, and for the Trustees to provide a studentship so that university astronomers could travel to utilize the South African telescope.[64] Despite his distressing experience in 1907, Turner trusted Knox-Shaw and Frank Dyson, who since May 1929 was a Radcliffe Trustee, and believed that valuable international co-operation would result. Thus he carried his Visitors to a formal public support of the Trustees, the future benefactor for astronomy in Oxford.

However, Turner's faculty colleague Professor F. A. Lindemann (later Lord Cherwell) began to mount a very vigorous opposition. He had taken over the Clarendon Physics Laboratory in 1919, and since then had struggled to modernize it, not least because he had found it extremely difficult to build a research team there. He now portrayed the Nuffield money as a benefaction to the Trustees that they were bound to spend within the University by building an observatory on one of the adjacent hills; this would be an Institute for Cosmical Physics, which besides astronomy would include branches of atmospheric physics, meteorology and geophysics. Lindemann was extremely able, witheringly sarcastic to his opponents and utterly ruthless. He approached both Trustees and University officers behind Turner's back, and by 5 February had undermined Turner's previously unanimous support and had browbeaten colleagues on the Board of the Faculty of Physical Sciences into passing a formal resolution deploring the expatriation of this 'endowment for Oxford science'. While stressed by this, and by the prospect of a cut in one of the external grants that he relied on for routine work, Turner died of a stroke in August 1930.

Turner's successor to the Savilian chair in 1932 was the young Canadian astrophysicist Harry H. Plaskett (1893–1980) who took the post on the very shrewdly negotiated condition that the University would equip him with a new solar telescope irrespective of the outcome of their legal dispute with the Trustees. He was duly able to advance his plans without delay, completed the new telescope in 1935, dropped elementary astronomy lectures for undergraduates, and instead lectured in astrophysics in order to attract applied mathematicians and physics students. In co-operation with his friend and colleague Professor E. A. Milne (1896–1950), they established a School of Astrophysics between 1933 and 1939 that was to become very successful. Meanwhile, in May 1931 at Lindemann's instigation the University began a legal action against the Trustees to prevent expatriation of the capital of Radcliffe's charitable Trust. Supported strongly by the Astronomer Royal, Sir Frank Dyson, the Trustees resisted with determination, but it was not until July 1934 that the case was decided in their favour.[65] Plaskett did gain because the Bird Bequest to assist the remuneration of an assistant was transferred to the University, and the Trustees established a Radcliffe Travelling Fellowship which was to prove very fertile in attracting some very able astrophysicists to spend part of their time in the University Observatory.

The Radcliffe Observatory was finally closed for astronomy in June 1935. However, the legal wrangle had wasted four precious years, and it was only in that year that Knox-Shaw placed the all-important contract with Grubb-Parsons for the new 1.8 metre (72 inch) reflecting telescope in South Africa – a revised choice of instrument that had been made in 1931, instead of taking the Double Refractor to South Africa. By 1939 Knox-Shaw was relocated to the completed new observatory but the mirror was delayed first by technical difficulties and then by the war, so was only delivered in 1948, while the vital spectrograph arrived in 1951, soon after his retirement. In the intervening decade he had only been able to use the great instrument's finder scope for direct photography. His vision was then triumphantly vindicated but post-war inflation meant that the Trust could no longer run the new observatory independently. In 1950 he negotiated a funding agreement with the British government by which one-third of the time on the telescope would go to observers from the Royal Observatory at the Cape. In 1974 the Radcliffe Reflector was purchased by the South African Astronomical Observatory (founded in 1972), and moved to the latter's site at Sutherland in the Northern Cape province.

An important link between the Radcliffe and University observatories was an Assistant, Frank A. Bellamy (1863–1936), who in July 1881 followed his two brothers who had been junior assistants at the Radcliffe Observatory, where at the age of 18 he learned to use the instruments, and later had charge of the photography and then also of meteorology. In 1892 he joined the University Observatory, and was First Assistant there until 1936, a career of 55 years serving Oxford astronomy. Fiercely loyal to Turner, but a man who could be controversial when provoked, Bellamy was bitterly opposed to Professor Plaskett turning the University Observatory to astrophysics, and equally chagrined that the Radcliffe Observatory was closing down. Whenever the directors were away he scoured both observatories, listing and labelling the old instruments, and hiding some. He then wrote notes to Robert T. Gunther, who had founded the Museum of the History of Science in Oxford in 1927, urging him to apply for this or that apparatus. Bellamy's concern to preserve the past, and his own physical efforts when past the age of 70, certainly helped to gather and save much material.[66]

Knox-Shaw himself was inclined to preserve as much of the old instrumentation as possible. One of Bird's mural quadrants of 1773 and the heliometer (because Gunther had no space for it) were given to the Science Museum in London, and can be viewed in the store there. The other Bird quadrant and the zenith sector, Hornsby's portable 32 inch Bird quadrant, the two Dollond refractors, the Herschel reflector of 1812, the Jones Mural Circle of 1836 and the Carrington Transit Circle of 1854, are all displayed in the Museum of the History of Science, Oxford. The Grubb Double Refractor, refused by Oxford University in 1935 because it was beyond the remit or resources of the University Observatory to operate, was accepted with alacrity by London University, and installed at their Mill Hill Observatory, another major instrument passing from private to university use. In the 1990s it was given a very extensive refurbishment, so that beyond its centenary year it is in beautiful condition and in constant use for research and teaching. This work includes taking the third epoch plates to extend the value of Rambaut's and Knox-Shaw's work on proper motions in the Kapteyn Areas. The 10 inch Barclay Refractor was given to Marlborough College, where after complete refurbishment it was brought back in to use in 2003.[67]

Summary

The Introduction to this chapter identified resourcing the annual operation and instrument renewal as a recurring problem for observatories. Although in 1795 the Radcliffe Observatory was the finest in Europe, its meridian work was extremely onerous for a small staff. The expensive re-equipment with the heliometer in 1848 was the first attempt to enable the Radcliffe Observatory to undertake some of the new specialist work beyond the meridian. The instrument's technical problems, and the need for two men to work it, meant that it never fulfilled its potential. The Double Refractor of 1902 was intended to restore the Observatory to the international front rank. That attempt was increasingly frustrated by the Oxford climate and light pollution, and the incomparably greater resources of the leading American observatories. Astronomy had become internationally highly competitive. The Radcliffe Observatory remained a private institution, divorced from academic utility, and so the problem of resources became acute because it fell upon the Trust alone; there was no incentive for private benefactors to assist. In contrast, at Cambridge University in the 1890s, Hugh. F. Newall erected, financed, and gave to the University a complete astrophysical observatory on the University's existing site, a benefaction which attracted endowment for research students and led directly to the University integrating astronomical research into its examined curriculum and thereby stimulated further gifts.

The second issue was the evolving relationships between the Trustees and their Observers with the University. On one hand the Trust was a major benefactor of the city and the University (through the Infirmary), of the University (through the Radcliffe Camera and later the Science Library), and of astronomy (because the Observatory always provided a few of the crucial professional posts in the country). On the other hand, the major re-equipment of their Observatory in 1902, when the 'new' University Observatory of 1875 was already struggling to fulfil both research and teaching roles, blighted Professor Turner's hopes for any improvement, and left Cambridge unchallenged to make astrophysics its own before 1935. The two issues coincided with renewed force in 1929. To remain relevant in international astronomy, the Radcliffe Observer Knox-Shaw was determined to move to South Africa. The Trustees were willing – not least because as true philanthropists they recognized the city's need to expand the Infirmary on to their Observatory site. Suffice to say that, once the Observatory had moved, astronomy at Oxford began to thrive under Professor Harry H. Plaskett, because it was no longer the target of cost cutters within the University and because Plaskett wisely used his assumption of office as the lever to obtain new equipment for astrophysics in 1933. This brought graduate research within the curriculum, had the benefit of appointing Radcliffe Travelling Fellows to work in Pretoria and Oxford, and upgraded the professorial lectures to teaching more advanced maths and physics undergraduates.

The working achievements of the Radcliffe Observatory across the 161 years from 1773 to 1934 were, cumulatively, considerable. Hornsby's and his colleagues' publication of Bradley's superb observations provided the material that Encke capitalized on in Berlin. Therefore, at a time when governments were desperate to find a reliable means for mariners to establish longitude at sea, the Germans demonstrated the method. In the mid-nineteenth century, when the universities lacked the money available to the leading amateur savants, the University Observatory directors learned caution in technological innovation from the Radcliffe's bold experiment with the heliometer. Arguably that saved more than one vulnerable university observatory, although each needed to escape from meridian work. It is no accident that when Professor Pritchard built the University of Oxford's Observatory in 1875, he chose to equip it with a modest, conventional 12 inch refractor. He flourished briefly while Edward Stone was frustrated, and Pritchard's successor Turner developed photographic star mapping but would soon overreach his own resources. Stone's frustrations in the 1880s and 1890s became the opportunity for his successor Rambaut to argue irresistibly for a first class photographic instrument, and to tackle a suitably limited and useful area of research. Those two steps ensured that the Radcliffe Observatory regained its status in the international front rank after a lapse of 80 years. The successive Observers and Assistants, quietly if not always patiently working for very modest salaries, usually until the day they literally dropped, enabled the Observatory to weather the fluctuating Trust resources and professional challenges. Thus the Observatory survived usefully until in Knox-Shaw it found another inspired Director who between 1929 and 1933 mustered university, national and international support for a plan that promised great benefits to all concerned. It was only the combination of delay caused by legal opposition in 1933 and the onset of war in 1939 that crippled the Radcliffe Observatory's postwar future as an independent institution. Nevertheless, British astronomy then gained access to a world class large reflector on a superb southern hemisphere site.

In late 1934 the Radcliffe Observatory finally lay empty of its handful of astronomers, their chests of star charts, their piles of reductions and catalogue proofs, their cabinets of first and second epoch photographs, the accumulated notes of a century's meteorological observations, and the files of the Observers' correspondence. In the two years 1934–5 Harold Knox-Shaw disposed of the contents as constructively as possible. Inevitably there was considerable controversy when the famed library was dispersed, much of it at auction. He took care to ensure that the historic instruments were all given to appropriate museums or observatories. The Observatory's papers were eventually transferred by the Trust to the Bodleian Library. The small heliometer tower in the south garden was empty. Frank Bellamy no longer made clandestine visits to salvage objects that he so feared would be discarded. Now the Observatory was all but engulfed by the spreading city, silent, bare, grimy and in need of paint, bereft of instruments, home only to the ghosts of the astronomers and their loved ones who had died in the elegant house. Hornsby had enjoyed his Observatory for 36 years and his children grew up there. Abraham Robertson grew old alone there. Rigaud's children played and laughed in the garden. Manuel Johnson and his wife made the house familiar by their hospitality while their children grew up there. Stone harboured his local frustrations while doing the best he could, and enjoying his reputation in London. Rambaut won many friends in Oxford and had the drive to realize a dream, but Knox-Shaw understood that it could not continue on the city site, and he brought the Observatory to address the national need.

These men led a century and a half of aspirations, unremitting hard work, and the achievement of much good observational astronomy. If it were not all cutting edge research in its own time, it nevertheless contributed to the essential international corpus of comparable observations: the sum being more valuable than the parts. In 1935 the Observatory passed from the Trustees via the generosity of Lord Nuffield, to the city council. The future lay dependent upon the aspirations and initiatives of men and women of a very different science.

NOTES

1. Simcock, A. V. (1984) *The Ashmolean Museum and Oxford Science 1683-1893*. Oxford Museum of the History of Science, Oxford. 11-12 and fn.108; Chapman, A. (1993) James Bradley, 1693-1762: an Oxford Astronomer in Eclipse. *Oxford Magazine*, Fourth Week, Trinity term. 17-19.

2. Warrant of Charles II, dated 22nd June 1675. Cited: Grant, R. (1852, second edition 1966) *History of Physical Astronomy*. Johnson Reprint, London. 460.

3. For the problem of finding position at sea, see the superb website *The Discovery of Longitude: An Historical Account of Maritime Navigational Practice and the Subsequent Invention of the Chronometer* by Jonathan Medwin (1977) www.rubens.anu.edu.au/student.projects97/naval; also: Williams, J. E. D. (1992) *From Sails to Satellites. The Origin and Development of Navigational Science*. Oxford University Press, Oxford. Quotation cited 80.

4. Chapman, A. (1993) Pure research and practical teaching: the astronomical career of James Bradley, 1693-1762. *Notes and Records of the Royal Society of London*. 47:2: 205-12.

5. Hutchins, R. (forthcoming 2006) *British University Observatories c. 1820-1939*. Ashgate Publishing Ltd, Hampshire. (Publication of D.Phil. Thesis, University of Oxford, 1999.)

6. Smith, R. W. (1991) A national observatory transformed: Greenwich in the nineteenth century. *Journal of the History of Astronomy*. 22: 5-20.

7. These evolving and often contentious issues for the five observatories are fully analyzed in Hutchins (forthcoming 2006).

8. Guest, I. (1991) *John Radcliffe and his Trust.* The Radcliffe Trust, London. Ch. VI; Rambaut, A. A. (1918) The Radcliffe Observatory. In, Nias, J. B. (Ed) *Dr John Radcliffe, a Sketch of his Life with an Account of his Fellows and Foundations etc.* Clarendon Press, Oxford. 117-23; Rigaud, S. P. (1836) *Memorials of Oxford.* Pamphlet, Oxford. 9pp; Turner, G. L. E. (1986) The physical sciences. In: Sutherland, L. S. and Mitchell, L. G. (Eds) *The History of the University of Oxford. V The Eighteenth Century.* Oxford University Press, Oxford. 659-81.

9. For an excellent explanation of the importance of the Venus transit, of Hornsby's extensive analysis of the several 1761 results, and of the observations made by Cook and astronomer Charles Green in 1769, see Howse, D. and Murray, A. (1997) Lieutenant Cook and the transit of Venus 1769. *Astronomy and Geophysics.* 38:4: 27-30.

10. Hornsby's original plan (1768) *S .P. Rigaud's Notebook,* 19-24, 19-20, Bodleian Library, Oxford, Radcliffe Trust Papers, Bodl. MS. d.d. Radcl. e.2.

11. Hornsby (1768) 3-4, and 20-21.

12. Rambaut (1918) 117-18.

13. Hornsby (1768) 20-21.

14. Paper 5-2-1771, Hornsby (1768) *Rigaud's Notebook.* 8.

15. In 2001 Michael Pirie of Green College located the position of the base of this building on the Ordnance Survey map of 1887, and an illustration of it.

16. Hornsby, T. 'Notes and Instructions, Oxford, Dec. 1785', MS. *Radcliffe 16,* Museum of the History of Science, Oxford; and Chapman, A. (1990) *Dividing the Circle, the Development of Critical Angular Measurement in Astronomy 1500-1850.* Ellis Horwood, Chichester. 86-7.

17. Bennett, J. A. (1990) *Church, State and Astronomy in Ireland: 200 Years of Armagh Observatory* Armagh Observatory and Institute of Irish Studies, Belfast. Cited 122 and 124.

18. Wallis, R. (2004) Hornsby, Thomas. *Oxford Dictionary of National Biography.* Oxford University Press, Oxford. 28: 169-70.

19. For more on Hornsby's observations, and his balancing of his work and plural offices, see Guest, (1991) 246-51; Hutchins (forthcoming 2006).

20. Guest (1991) 250-1.

21. Minutes of Trustees' meeting (7 June 1811) Bodleian Library MS. d.d. Radcl. c.52.

22. Minutes of Trustees' meeting (26 May 1812) Bodleian Library MS d.d. Radcl. c.52. Cited in full Guest (1991) 253.

23. Anon (February 1827) Abraham Robertson *Gentleman's Magazine* 97: 176-8.

24. Thackeray, A. D. (1972) *The Radcliffe Observatory, 1772-1972.* The Radcliffe Trust, London. 9.

25. Dreyer, J. L. E. and Turner, H. H. (1987) *History of the Royal Astronomical Society* London. 1: 57.

26. Anon. Mr Rigaud. *Memoirs Royal Astronomical Society.* XI: 184: 321-3, Hutchins, R. (2004) Rigaud, Stephen Peter. *Oxford Dictionary of National Biography.* Oxford University Press, Oxford. 46: 966-8.

27. His *Report on the Astronomical Instruments in the Radcliffe Observatory at Oxford,* RAS Archive G.1 (unnumbered) is reproduced in Guest (1991) 257-8.

28. Chapman (1990) 120-2.

29. Trustees' Minutes, quoted by solicitors Longbourne, Stevens and Powell to A. D. S. Leake, solicitor for the Charity Commissioners (31 March 1930) Cambridge University Library, Royal Greenwich Observatory Archive, RGO 48, Radcliffe p. 10, para 15.

30. The patronage network for astronomy, Airy's influence, and elections to the Radcliffe Observership, are analysed in Hutchins (forthcoming 2006).

31. Dewhirst, D. W. (1985) Meridian astronomy in the private and university observatories of the United Kingdom: rise and fall. *Vistas in Astronomy.* 28: 147-58, 152.

32. [Robert Main] (1860) Manuel John Johnson. *Monthly Notices of the Royal Astronomical Society* (MNRAS) XX: 4: 123-30.

33. Guest (1991) 263.

34. Sampson, R. A. (1923) *History of the RAS.* I: (1987 edition, Royal Astronomical Society) 89-90; *Memoirs RAS* (1851) XX: 221.

35. Hutchins (2004) Pogson, Norman Robert, *Dictionary of National Biography*. Oxford. 44: 678-80.

36. [Main] (1860) Manuel Johnson. *MNRAS*. XX: 4: 123-30, 129.

37. W. F. Donkin to H. Acland, note Nov 12 (1859) Bodl. MS d.d. Radcl. c.40-2.

38. Airy to Trustees, letter (1 April 1859). RGO 6: 146; 7: 253.

39. Airy to Pogson, letter (23 May 1859). RGO 6: 146; 7: 256.

40. Opinion of Dr. Acland (9 March 1860) 8, Bodl. MS d.d. Radcl. c.40.

41. Herschel to Airy, letter (11 June 1859), RGO 6: 146; 8: 266.

42. Airy to S. Herbert (Radcliffe Trustee), letter (13 June 1859), Bodl. MS d.d. Radcl. c.40.

43. Airy to Gill at Dun Echt Observatory, letter (31 January 1872), RGO 6: 150: 236.

44. John Glaisher, assistant at Cambridge, to James Challis, letter (nd. May 1838), *Camb. Observatory Archive 1838*. 38.

45. Sheepshanks to Challis, letter (11 August 1851), Cambridge Observatory Archive 1851. 27.

46. Challis to Airy, Draft for Visitors, (26 October 1855) Camb. Obs. Archive 1855. 31.

47. Airy to Keating, letter (17 August 1870) RGO 6: 160: 48.

48. *Report of the Radcliffe Observer to the Trustees* (June 1867) 7. Bodl. MS d.d. Radcl. c.40.

49. For an obituary portraying the labour intrinsic to the responsibility for publishing star catalogues, see Dunkin, E. (1879) Rev. Robert Main. *Obituary Notices of Astronomers*. Royal Astronomical Society, London. 165-88.

50. Hutchins, R. (1994) John Phillips, geologist-astronomer, and the origins of the Oxford University Observatory, 1853-75. *History of Universities*. Oxford. XIII: 194-249.

51. Airy (8 June 1878) Official remarks by the Astronomer Royal etc. Bodl. MS d.d. Radcl. c.40.

52. Corr: Pritchard with Airy (1878) ROG 6: 153: 141-244.

53. Letter, Turner to Christie, Oxford (20 July 1897) RGO 7: 156, Radcliffe Obs.

54. Wayman, P. A. (2004) Rambaut, Arthur Alcock. *Oxford Dictionary of National Biography*. Oxford. 45: 889-90.

55. See Howarth, J. (1987) Science education in late–Victorian Oxford: a curious case of failure? *English Historical Review*. 102: 335-71 and 366-7.

56. Brierly, J. L. (1927) Anson, Sir William Reynell, *Dictionary of National Biography 1912-21*. 8-10: 9.

57. Turner to Anson, letters (13 and 16 March 1907) Bodl. Anson Corr. 26 and 29.

58. Turner, H. H. (1907) The attitude of Oxford towards observation and experiment. Letter to *The Times*, 23 March 1907. 6.

59. Anson, W. R. (1907) Letter to *The Times*, 28 March 1907. 10.

60. Turner, 'Radcliffe and University Observatories', Bodleian Library MS d.d. Radcl. c.42. p. 5.

61. Anson's proposal is cited Guest (1992) 300. But Anson's private 'prompt sheet', *Anson Corr.* p. 33 shows that Anson was acting as the economic conscience of the University.

62. Ivor Guests's (1992) account is excellent from the viewpoint of the Trustees. Jack Morrell in his *Science at Oxford 1914-1939: Transforming an Arts University* (Oxford, Clarendon. 1997. 248-55), ably portrays the interests of all parties, but is too dismissive of the pressures that bore upon Professor Turner. His and the astronomers' viewpoint is covered in Hutchins (forthcoming 2006).

63. Thackeray, A. D. (1971) Harold Knox-Shaw, *Quarterly Journal of the RAS*. 12: 197-201.

64. *Minutes of the Visitors to the University Observatory* (30 January 1930) Oxford University Archive, UDC/M/36/1: 140.

65. Guest (1992) cites fully from the Trustees' papers, but to complement his clear portrayal of the Trust's position with an account of Turner's position and the effect of the dispute upon astronomy in the University, see Hutchins (1999).

66. Hutchins, R. (2004) Bellamy, Frank Arthur. *Oxford Dictionary of National Biography*. Oxford University Press, Oxford. 4: 985-7.

67. Barclay, C. (2003) Victorian Phoenix. *Astronomy Now*. February 2003. 75-6.

Plate 41. Stephen Rigaud, Savilian Professor and
Observer 1827-39
(*Museum of the History of Science, Oxford*)

Plate 42. Manuel Johnson, Radcliffe Observer
1839-59 (*Royal Astronomical Society Library*)

Plate 43. Robert Main, Radcliffe Observer
1860-78 (*Royal Astronomical Society Library*)

Plate 44. Edward Stone, Radcliffe Observer
1879-97 (*Royal Astronomical Society Library*)

Plate 45. Arthur Rambaut, Radcliffe Observer
1897-24 (*courtesy The Radcliffe Trust*)

Plate 46. Harold Knox-Shaw, Radcliffe
Observer 1924-50
(*Royal Astronomical Society Library*)

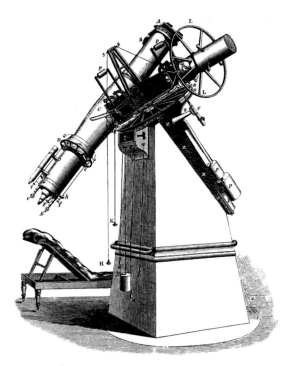

Plate 47. The Radcliffe Heliometer, drawn by Mrs Annarella Smyth, engraving from Captain W. H. Smyth, *Speculum Hartwellianum,* 1860

Plate 48. The Reverend Robert Main with the Wellington Telescope mounted beside the Heliometer tower (*Bodleian Library, Oxford, courtesy The Radcliffe Trust*)

Plate 49. The Carrington Transit Circle of 1854
(*The Bodleian Library, Oxford, courtesy The Radcliffe Trust*)

Plate 50. The Grubb 24 inch photographic and 18 inch visual telescopes (the 'Double Equatorial') of 1903, with Harold Knox-Shaw on the observing chair
(*The Bodleian Library, Oxford, courtesy The Radcliffe Trust*)

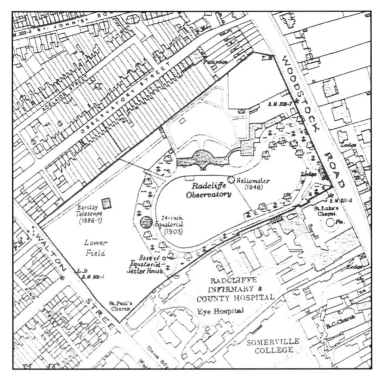

Plate 51. Plan of the Observatory Site adapted from the Ordnance Survey map of 1887 showing the location of the instruments housed in the grounds of the Observatory (*courtesy The Radcliffe Trust*)

Plate 52. The Radcliffe Observatory main building and new tower from ESE, 1922. The Heliometer Tower, since 1907 occupied by the 10 inch Barclay Refractor, is centre; the much larger Double Equatorial Tower is to the left beyond (*Bodleian Library, Oxford, courtesy The Radcliffe Trust*)

Plate 53. The meteorological station at Green College

Chapter 5

Meteorological Observation at the Radcliffe Observatory

Gordon Wallace

People everywhere have always taken an interest in the weather. Extremes are especially noteworthy. In Oxford there are tales of three successive exceptional winters from 1878/9 to 1880/81[1] and folk memories of Ice Fairs on the Thames. Who does not have some story of flooding or drought, windstorm or rainstorm? The first international conference on meteorology took place in Brussels as long ago as 1853.

From early times there has been scientific speculation about the envelope of air around us, and investigation of its properties. Aristotle wrote a treatise on it, his *Meteorologica*, by which term he meant the study of the processes, conditions and phenomena of the atmosphere. The idea of measuring atmospheric humidity by weighing a piece of sponge is attributed to Leonardo da Vinci; and Galileo is credited with measuring the weight of the atmosphere itself. Descartes produced his theory of rain in 1637, Halley his global wind chart in 1686, and Lamarck his classification of clouds in 1802. Christopher Wren was credited by the Royal Society with being the first person to make practical use of the barometer for weather purposes. Farmers and naturalists such as Gilbert White of Selborne have long kept records of the weather and how the weather affects crops, wild flowers, bird migration and the like.

The reason for making careful and exact measurements of temperature and humidity at the Radcliffe and other astronomical observatories is somewhat different. In addition to discovering the annual aberration of starlight (arising from the earth's orbital motion round the sun) and the nutation or nodding of the earth's pole (resulting from the attraction of moon and sun on the earth's equatorial bulge) James Bradley, an outstanding practical observer and Savilian Professor of Astronomy at Oxford from 1721 until his death in 1762, also discovered atmospheric refraction. This is a bending of light waves as they pass from the vacuum of space into the earth's atmosphere, thus displacing the apparent direction of the star or other celestial body from its true position by an amount that varies according not only to the observed altitude of the body but also to the pressure and temperature of the atmosphere at the point of observation. It was immediately recognized that in order to obtain correct observations of stars it would be necessary to calibrate the atmospheric effect by making exact observations of pressure and temperature at an observatory's site. Measurements of humidity were also made but later.

Justification of the expenditure falling on the trustees, or on the public purse in officially supported observatories, was found in the needs of mariners for accurate star maps, and also in the need to predict seasonal wind and weather patterns over the oceans. By the nineteenth century drought and famine conditions in different parts of the Empire, especially in India, made the study of meteorology a natural and financially justifiable extension of the useful work of any observatory.

The establishment of observatories in western Europe

Two observatories, financed by governments, have been of particular importance to the development of meteorology in Western Europe.

The Paris Observatory, established in 1667, was created to further the study and observation of celestial and atmospheric phenomena. Its continuous temperature and rainfall records date from 1785, and there is an earlier brief record of weather in Paris dating back to 1658.[2] A Meteorology Division was set up under J-B Lamarck in 1796 and Lamarck's *Annuaire météorologique* was published from 1800 until terminated after the eleventh volume, of 1810, by order of Napoleon *'choqué qu'un membre de l'Institut s'amuse à faire des prédictions'*. Ironically, Napoleon had to go back to Lamarck later for a forecast of the likely weather in Western Russia in the autumn and winter of 1812. Lamarck gave him the correct response that really severe weather usually did not set in before January. Unfortunately for Napoleon's Grande Armée the bitter winter of 1812–13 arrived early in October 1812.

The Greenwich Observatory was created, pragmatically enough, by Charles II to promote astronomy and in particular to provide observations that would advance the art of navigation. It was established in 1675 and immediately busied itself with astronomical observations. Temperature and rainfall records there date from 1771.

However it was not till 1838 that a separate Magnetic and Meteorology Department was set up under the inspired James Glaisher. This reflected the speculation that sunspots might be caused by or linked to magnetic phenomena, and that sunspot cycles might directly affect weather on earth. Glaisher's first daily weather reports date from 1851, although these lasted only a few weeks in the first instance.

The Radcliffe Observatory, founded a century after Paris and Greenwich, was one of a number of European observatories set up in the second half of the eighteenth century. With the exception of the Royal Observatory at Kew, few of these new institutions contributed to the development of observational or theoretical meteorology as much as the Radcliffe Observatory eventually did.

Systematic meteorological observations have been undertaken elsewhere in and around Oxford, for example at Magdalen College and at Wytham on the outskirts of Oxford where there is a University farm. These observations are not considered here.

Oxford University in the time of Hornsby, first Radcliffe Observer

Over the seventeenth and eighteenth centuries a new Enlightenment had been creeping into France, the Netherlands, England, Germany and Scotland. However, Oxford and Cambridge Universities were very slow to incorporate new ideas or introduce new courses. Before 1760 Oxford was a 'Tory and High-Anglican enclave in defiant opposition to the Whig and latitudinarian mainstream'.[3] Many Oxford academics deliberately resisted change on the grounds that the primary function of the university was to demonstrate the truths of Christianity, rather than to free the mind from 'the bondage of unreason'. Oxford's undergraduate curriculum was held to have 'no use in the real world' and although some classroom lectures were given in scientific subjects those subjects were not examined.

In those days university dons tended to be in Holy Orders in order to have the option of a benefice and, in the case of Christ Church Canons, to marry. (College Fellows generally were required to remain unmarried.) Salaries were low, there were no retirement schemes, no pensions and no comfortable north Oxford homes to retire to. To make a living, teaching staff sought to maximize the number of teaching posts they held and to remain in post until they dropped. Yet there were few obligations on Professors to give regular lectures themselves, and it was not uncommon for them to delegate such mundane duties to assistants, some of whom were ill-qualified for the task. As for the Tutors, they were expected to tutor each student over the full range of his studies and set books, so that specialization became virtually impossible for them.

Hornsby, the heir of Halley and Bradley and their recently established practice of experimental science, was one of a new breed of scholars who helped the University to drag itself into the modern age.[4] There was a long rearguard action from the clerical faction. It was not until the departure of John Henry Newman and some of his colleagues for Rome around 1845 that the air cleared somewhat and those who remained Anglican in persuasion attempted, with some relief, to turn to more profitable studies. (Cardinal Newman's last night in Oxford was spent in the Observer's House.)

Unfortunately, many of those who remained now believed that everything worth studying could be found in the Classics. The Honour School of Natural Science was founded only in 1850 when the University, anticipating criticism by the pending Royal Commission enquiring into the state of the universities, conceded that they would build a museum to house the five professors of natural science and realized that the University would have to provide a taught and examined syllabus. Manuel Johnson, fourth Radcliffe Observer, was a member of the delegacy set up to obtain architectural plans and estimates and to advise Convocation as to the most suitable design.

It was not until the late 1850s and the opening of the University Museum in 1860 that ideas such as those of Charles Lyell, A. R. Wallace, and Charles Darwin could begin to take general hold. Such was the condition of the University against which we have to understand the work of the early Radcliffe Observers.

1772–1810 first Radcliffe Observer, Thomas Hornsby

Thomas Hornsby (1733–1810) was a noted pluralist. Master of Arts in 1757 he was elected Fellow of Corpus Christi. He was appointed Savilian Professor of Astronomy and consequently elected a Fellow of the Royal Society in 1763. He was appointed Radcliffe Observer in 1772, Sedleian Professor of Natural Philosophy (a mathematical chair) in 1782, Reader in Experimental Philosophy (the subject that is now physics) in 1783 and Radcliffe Librarian in the same year. All of these posts he held until his death aged seventy six. In 1785 he qualified, by Diploma, as Doctor of Divinity.

When Hornsby succeeded James Bradley as Savilian Professor of Astronomy at the start of 1763, the requirement of yearly courses was introduced.[5] He did subsequently employ a deputy – Stephen Rigaud, later third Radcliffe Observer – to deliver at least some of his Experimental Philosophy lectures for him but it was also claimed for him that 'though subject to epilepsy . . [he] . . . had delivered a perspicuous course each term to classes which generally numbered over fifty.'[6]

Hornsby's principal accomplishment lay in persuading the Radcliffe Trustees to build their fine Observatory (see Chapters 1 and 3) but he is also remembered largely for the high quality of his experimental work. He sent in to the Royal Society careful observations of the solar eclipse of 1 April 1764 and subsequently his observations of the transit of Venus of 3 June 1769. This was the transit of Venus viewed by James Cook and Joseph Banks from Tahiti for the Royal Society.[7]

Hornsby took the opportunity at the same time to give exact (and admirably correct) details of the latitude of Oxford (51 degrees, 45 minutes, 15 seconds) as determined by himself from observations of the Pole Star; and also of the longitude of Oxford, 5 minutes, 3 seconds or 5 minutes, 4 seconds to the West of Greenwich, based on a comparison of his observations of the Sun's eclipse at Oxford and observations made at Greenwich. This was a fine result – nowadays we take it to be 5 minutes, 2.6 seconds.

From 1767 Hornsby is known to have made regular meteorological observations from the roof of the professor's house in New College Lane where Edmund Halley had built a small teaching observatory.[8] Several of Hornsby's early meteorological records survive and are held in the archives of Oxford's School of Geography. These records form the basis of a reconstruction by the Craddocks of the rainfall at Oxford from 1767 to 1814.[9]

Hornsby's meteorological observations from the new Radcliffe Observatory site started at ground level as early as 1774, shortly after the ground floor rooms were built. He had taken up residence there and started astronomical observations in 1773.

We know that Hornsby had a 12 inch copper funnel for his principal rain gauge made for him by a reputable maker and that in the first instance he probably weighed the rain collected rather than measuring it in a graduated glass vessel.[10] The barometer he used was probably the fine instrument made by Bird in 1773, now in the Museum of the History of Science in Broad Street, Oxford. It is not clear what thermometers he used nor where these were located but we do know that

Hornsby insisted on having instruments from the finest London makers.

For a variety of reasons – lack of funds and lack of an assistant, overwork, old age, and eventually ill health – Hornsby did not publish his meteorological observations. However, they were carefully made with sound instruments, and now form an important element in the longest continuous series of temperature and rainfall records from any one site in the British Isles.

1810–26 second Radcliffe Observer, Abram Robertson

Born and bred in the Scottish Borders, Abram – sometimes written Abraham – Robertson (1751-1826) arrived in Oxford with empty pockets and an optimistic expectation that he would easily find employment there in teaching mathematics.[11] He was obliged for a time to take a post as a domestic servant but his mathematical abilities soon earned him a servitorship at Christ Church. (A servitor was an undergraduate member of his college who was excused lecture fees and who received free or nearly free board and lodging, originally in exchange for some domestic or personal service.) In time Robertson advanced from this post and he was in due course appointed deputy to the Savilian Professor of Geometry. John Smith MD, the professor in question, was a doctor of medicine non-resident in Oxford having gone off to practise medicine as a general practitioner in Cheltenham! (His *Observations on the Use and Abuse of the Cheltenham Waters* was published in 1786.) As his deputy at Oxford Robertson gave lectures that were held 'in great repute'.[12]

Robertson's principal published works were mathematical books and papers. He was a great admirer of Isaac Newton's 'transcendant abilities' as displayed in his *Mathematical Principles of Natural Philosophy (Philosophiae Naturalis Principia Mathematica)* publication of which was complete by 1687.

Robertson employed and supervised an assistant in making some astronomical observations and made three main contributions to the observatory's meteorological work: firstly he purchased for the Observatory a number of good quality meteorological instruments and introduced from 1816 more systematic observations of pressure and temperature; secondly, he completed the task of obtaining the freehold over the land on which the new Observatory had been built; lastly, in 1822, he persuaded the *Edinburgh Philosophical Journal* to publish the Radcliffe Meteorological results for 1816-21, the first meteorological results of the Radcliffe Observatory to be published. In this paper he showed that the observed results for Oxford did not bear out certain contentions, such as that of Dr Brewster, subsequently Sir David Brewster and Vice-Chancellor of Edinburgh University, that the mean annual temperature of a place on a particular meridian could be reduced to a mathematical function of its latitude. Brewster's formula in this case was $T = 81\frac{1}{2} \cos$ latitude.

1827-39 third Radcliffe Observer, Stephen Peter Rigaud

Born at Richmond, Surrey, the young Stephen Rigaud (1774-1839) came up to Exeter College in 1791 aged about 17. Three years later, while he was still too young to be appointed a Tutor, he was elected a Fellow of the College, though he had not yet taken his BA. In 1805 he gave lecture demonstrations on Experimental Philosophy for the ailing Thomas Hornsby. In 1810 he succeeded Hornsby as Reader in Experimental Philosophy, and Robertson as Savilian Professor of Geometry. In 1814 he succeeded his father as Observer to the King at the Kew Observatory. In 1827 he succeeded Robertson as Radcliffe Observer and Savilian Professor of Astronomy, at which time he gave up his Chair of Geometry.

Rigaud was a competent astronomer who subsequently became primarily the leading historian of mathematics and of astronomy. He accumulated a renowned library of scientific books and papers and it is through him that so much is known about Isaac Newton. Rigaud also edited the works and correspondence of James Bradley, Hornsby's predecessor.

Rigaud took a scientific interest in weather as a continuous natural phenomenon, rather than regarding the weather as merely an aid or hindrance to astronomical observation. He recognized the interdependence of the various meteorological elements and starting in 1828, organized the taking daily of three complete sets of eye observations of all the main meteorological elements at the Radcliffe Observatory. Self-registering maximum and minimum thermometers were obtained. Starting in June 1838, Rigaud brought into use as his main barometer the splendid Newman Standard No. 1220 that still graces the downstairs Common Room of Green College.

Rigaud wrote an excellent meteorological paper, *Remarks on the Proportionate Quantities of Rain in Different Seasons at Oxford*,[13] in which he analyzed and discussed the rainfall patterns for the twenty years 1815 to 1834. The rain was collected in a vessel using the 12 inch copper funnel made originally for Hornsby, sited at different dates on the parapet of the Observatory's east wing at heights of 22 and 24 feet.

Rigaud was well aware that not enough was known about what he called the 'chemical affinities' of the atmosphere; nor of the appropriate weights to be attributed to different variables such as atmospheric pressure, temperature, wind direction, and elevation; nor of the effects upon those variables of the proximity of neighbouring oceans or continental masses. 'But there can be no doubt' he wrote, 'that patient investigation will eventually lead us to a general knowledge of their several influences.'

Without naming his source, he then quoted some pious verse:

> . . . . the first Almighty Cause Acts not by partial but by general laws;

Rigaud considered that it was too early an epoch to speculate yet on the causes of weather phenomena and claimed that he would confine himself to giving a digest of the facts. However, he was not above massaging the facts to suit his beliefs. He decided to omit data from his final year 1834. He thought 1834 anomalous and he saw some advantage in using a period of nineteen years, his 'golden number, or Metonic Cycle, at the end of which the new moons return again . . . so as to coincide with the same days of the several months.'[14] Needless to say Rigaud came inevitably to the conclusion that whatever the influence of the moon upon terrestrial weather, the current understanding of it was insufficient to be useful for weather prediction.

In considering the rainfall in each month Rigaud found great variation from year to year. Several months turned out to be the wettest month of some years and the driest month of other years. None the less, he decided that the three months January to March were in general the driest of the year, with a total precipitation of less than one sixth of the annual rainfall. April to June, he found, averaged rather less than one quarter of the annual rainfall, being wettest in April and becoming drier into May and driest in June. Rainfall tended to increase steadily from July to September and then to diminish from October onwards. Despite the many uncertainties, Rigaud was sure 'that there has been a certain order, which probably is of no casual description'.[15]

1839-59 fourth Radcliffe Observer, Manuel John Johnson

Manuel Johnson (1805-59) was a man of action and an experienced practical observer. Born in Macao, he was first employed by The Honourable East India Company as an Artillery Officer and came late to scholarship. He was sent to Saint Helena where he immediately threw himself into the task of building a small astronomical observatory. He then observed and published a catalogue of 600 stars of the southern hemisphere, to the great benefit of British and other navigators.

Appointed Radcliffe Observer in 1839, at first with only one assistant, he directed the principal astronomical work to re-observing a limited number of circumpolar stars. This fully stretched his meagre resources

The unscreened principal thermometer, the measurements of which were read by eye, had previously been hung on the north facing wall of the east wing of the Observatory. In 1840 Johnson had it moved to a similar position on the west wing (no sensible difference in reading was thought likely) and in 1849 he was able to have it placed in a small screened penthouse, a wooden construction with a sloping roof, on the north side of the building. This penthouse remained in use, though with one move of a few feet, until 1878. After a period of comparison, the unscreened results from 1815 to 1849 were recalculated and reduced to the screened standard.

By 1 January 1853 a self-registering maximum and minimum thermometer was in use in the penthouse. From 1 January 1857 a sky radiation thermometer (grass minimum) and a solar radiation thermometer (sun maximum), both by Negretti and Zambra, were in use to the south of the Observatory building. From 1862 the minimum thermometers were moved and exposed over grass on the north lawn.

From 1853 Johnson used a 10 inch rain gauge on the south lawn – at a natural elevation of 206 feet above sea level – as his main gauge although the parapet gauge continued in use, being raised in 1862 from 22 to 24 feet to give a less sheltered exposure.

Johnson was responsible for two innovations that gave long term value to the Radcliffe Observatory's meteorological observations. First, he consolidated the systematic observations and, from 1847, he had these published together with the astronomical observations in the Observatory's annual *Results* volumes. Already a respected astronomer, he established the reputation of the Observatory for useful and standardized meteorology. From 1853 the Introductions to the annual volumes of *Results* expanded greatly and gave full details of the Observatory's meteorological procedures and its many innovations.

Johnson's second important contribution to meteorology was to introduce at the Radcliffe Observatory several self-recording instruments: barograph, thermograph and hygrograph in 1854; anemograph and pluviometer (or hyetograph) in 1856. Photographic equipment to keep accurate traces of the outputs of the first of these instruments was installed by William Crookes in 1854, beating Daguerre and the French observatories to automatic recording, doubtless to the chagrin of the French.

Twelve readings per day, at two-hourly intervals, were deduced from the photographic traces of barograph, thermograph and hygrograph. The results were published for some years in the Radcliffe annual volumes. Reproductions of the photographic traces of all of these instruments were published in 1857 for a variety of different types of weather (fine, cloudy, showery, rain, hail, etc.).

The detailed Radcliffe instrument readings were made available to researchers on the continent concerned to establish the relationship between atmospheric pressure and wind patterns, and seeking to reach some understanding of the propagation of weather across western Europe. Father Angelo Secchi, Director at the Vatican Observatory, made particular use of them and regretted that the French observatories of the time were unable to produce accurate timings for variations in pressure.

Like his predecessor, Johnson gave some thought to the influence of the moon on the weather. His 1854 volume of *Results* carried a table showing variations in barometric pressure tabulated according to the phases of the moon, lunation by lunation. However this was not repeated in later volumes. Perhaps in the meantime he had read a disparaging article in the *Philosophical Transactions of the Royal Society* by G. B. Airy, the Astronomer Royal, who had overheard a Norwegian sailor assert very positively that a northerly wind was to be expected at the time of the new moon. Airy got his assistant James Glaisher to draw up a table of some ninety lunations[16] from which it became clear that there was no such relationship between moon and wind.

From 1858 until 1875, using the Observatory's new self-recording instruments, very full details were established of the so-called 'diurnal inequalities'. Just as the oceans are subject to tides driven by the moon and in less degree the sun, so too is the atmosphere.

Johnson devoted much time, care and effort to constructing tables of long term mean values at the Radcliffe Observatory, hour by hour and month by month, for this atmospheric tidal effect. These tables were published in detail in the annual *Results* volumes of the Observatory. In effect what Johnson was seeking to do for observers' knowledge of atmospheric pressure in Oxford was to establish some base line that would bear the same relation to the fluctuating tides of the atmosphere as the base line of 'Ordnance datum' bears in relation to the tides of the oceans. It was believed that, when daily tidal effects on the atmosphere were stripped away, what would be left would be the 'true, mean monthly values' for the point of observation at any hour.

In these endeavours Johnson was much encouraged by James Glaisher. Not only had Glaisher taken charge of the Magnetic and

Meteorological Department of the Greenwich Observatory, he was a driving force in developing meteorological work in the country. Starting in 1847 Glaisher organized a voluntary system of precise meteorological observation throughout England. He prepared meteorological reports for the Registrar-General, helped to establish a daily weather report for the *Daily News*, was a founder of the Royal Meteorological Society and acted as its Secretary from 1850 to 1872. For the diurnal inequalities or horary changes of atmospheric pressure Glaisher constructed innumerable tables from around 1840 for the Greenwich Observatory and for the rooms in London of the Royal Society.

So, with Glaisher's support, and in the hope of establishing some underlying law or laws, values for the diurnal inequalities at Oxford were calculated and recorded in arithmetic form (the tables published in each annual volume), in geometric form (photographic curves from the self-registering instruments), and algebraic form (Bessel interpolation formulae).

This preoccupation with the diurnal inequalities seems to have been a peculiarly British one and continued long after it had been abandoned by leading meteorologists on the continent. For example, Professor Dove, Director of the Prussian Meteorological services, wrote in 1853 that the attention devoted to the diurnal variations was quite 'disproportionated to its subordinate interest'.[17] However, the Radcliffe Observatory continued to take diurnal variations very seriously until 1905 and beyond. It has to be admitted that the results of this particular preoccupation hardly justify the effort expended.

1860-78 fifth Radcliffe Observer, Robert Main

Before appointment to the Radcliffe Observatory, Robert Main (1808-78) had been the thoroughly competent First Assistant at the Royal Observatory, Greenwich.

As regards his meteorological work, while he did not expect the public to be interested, he carried out faithfully the duties of his post and ensured that the observations were made and published. In 1862 he arranged for a maximum and minimum thermometer to be brought into use at the top of the tower at a height of 105 feet above ground; and for more than twenty years simultaneous readings of this thermometer and the thermometers at ground level were published in the annual volumes. In the same year, 1862, he had the 10 inch rain gauge moved from the south lawn to a more exposed position at a natural elevation of about 208 feet on the north lawn. An 8 inch Glaisher gauge on the north lawn succeeded this older 10 inch gauge in 1877 with almost exactly the same exposure.

In 1872 the Radcliffe Observatory became a 'reporting station' to the Meteorological Office and from 1873 to 1913, its daily meteorological observations were telegraphed to the Meteorological Office to contribute to the preparation of synoptic charts and reports. Main also sent annual reports to the British (from 1884 'Royal') Meteorological Society, and these were duly published in the Society's journal.

From 1874 at the request of the Meteorological Office the Radcliffe Observatory participated in a US Government initiative proposed by General Meyer, USA, to make synchronous meteorological observations over the whole of the northern hemisphere. Observations in Oxford for that purpose were made from 1874 to 1886, initially at 45 minutes past midnight, later adjusted to midnight. Results of these observations were sent bi-monthly to the Meteorological Office for onward transmission to the US Signal Office, Washington DC, for publication in the *Bulletin of International Meteorological Observations*.

Influenced perhaps by the Meteorological Office, which began to issue daily weather charts in 1872, Main, in continuation of some work he had undertaken himself, encouraged a young lady of his acquaintance to give him some assistance by illustrating some of the Radcliffe *Results*. In his 1874 Report to the Trustees he wrote:[18]

As the temperatures depend upon the prevailing winds, and as these again are determined by the isobars or lines of equal pressure as distributed over large areas, it is evidently desirable that each observatory should furnish itself with the means of representing graphically the observed pressures. I am happy to say that, at my request and suggestion, this has been accomplished for Oxford by Miss Heurtley (daughter of the Reverend Canon Heurtley of Christ Church) who in the kindest way undertook the not inconsiderable labour of drawing the curves from 1859 to the year of the [Observatory's] last published volume of *Meteorological Observations* [1871] . . .

It would be interesting to know more about Miss Heurtley and whether she undertook any further meteorological or scientific work. Her name does not feature on the Observatory's lists of employees and it seems to disappear from the record immediately after Robert Main's 1874 report.

Despite these modest innovations and some equipment renewals, the *Introductions to the Meteorological Results* in the Radcliffe annual volumes suddenly become perfunctory ('Instruments and procedures continued substantially as in the previous year') following Main's appointment in 1860.

Nevertheless, Main was invited by Oxford's Ashmolean Society to read them a paper on the 'Rainfall of Oxford', which he did in December 1875, some forty years after Rigaud's paper on the same subject. Main's paper 'On the Rainfall for 25 Years (1851-1875)'[19] is interesting notwithstanding several disclaimers by Main himself.

He began by saying that 'The subject of Rainfall. . . partakes of the nature of all statistical enquiries, and is therefore to persons who have not a scientific or special interest in the subject, a very dull one.' Fortunately he did not make his paper any duller than it needed to be. He briefly outlined what he called 'the general theory of rainfall', listing three cases that correspond roughly to what would now be categorized as frontal rain (found at lines or planes separating air masses of different properties), orographic or relief rain (where winds forced over mountain barriers have to rise, with consequential cooling and precipitation of contained water vapour), and convectional rain (where warm ground surfaces cause thermal updrafts, leading to cooling and precipitation in the ascending air).

Main then proceeded to give some illustrative examples from all over the world which he freely admitted he had taken without further research from A. Buchan's *Meteorology*, a book that he heartily recommended.[20] (J. Bartholomew's great *Atlas of Meteorology*, Edinburgh, 1899, to which A. Buchan contributed so handsomely, is even more worthy of modern recommendation.) Main presented his tables of values for Oxford:

premising that the scientific interest in them will be but small, as I have not been able to discover any law of periodicity, or other facts which will justify any attempt at prediction.[21]

Among other things Main noticed that dry summers seemed to have been occurring at intervals of exactly ten years, specifically in 1854, 1864 and 1874. He thought, perhaps correctly, that this might be a mere casual coincidence and warned that 'nothing is more dangerous than to build theories upon a small induction of facts'. Observations over a longer period do suggest that there may be some periodicity of around ten years but the recurrence is far from regular and not confined to warm summers.

By 1876 the reliability of the autographic instruments was beginning to become suspect. Readings from the instruments continued to be made but, for the formulation of the published *Results* from 1 January 1876 until 29 February 1880, Main chose to rely on three daily sets of observations of the eye-read instruments, supplemented by indications of the self-registering thermometers.

The first five 'Newtonian' Observers

The first five Observers over the century from 1772 to 1878 shared a common view of science. They were all staunch Newtonians, and all five had a Newtonian vision of the heavens as God's creation, operating immutably according to His laws, with clockwork regularity and absolute depend-ability. Yet it was becoming clear that not everything would turn out to be fully predictable.

By the 1870s change was coming to be seen as part of the pattern. Up to the time of Johnson there appears to be an implicit underlying belief that if one could only strip away the tiresome vagaries of the actual daily weather, and such things as the tidal variations of the atmosphere, what would be left would be the 'true' weather of any given place. Yet rigorous exactitude was certainly not expected in the meteorological field. It was recognized that not just means but extremes, and the frequency of occurrence of extremes of different severity, would need to be taken into account in any scientific account of weather patterns.

Rigaud for one believed that in time we would reach an understanding of the true nature of weather as a matter of applied principles. By the time of Main we seem to have moved to a position where weather is seen essentially as a matter of statistics. Main thought that 'climatic meteorology'

would provide average values for every element of the climate of any place, together with the limits beyond which such values would be unlikely to vary. He considered it would never be possible to predict weather absolutely.

It was known that there had been Ice Ages in the past but most people probably thought of these as once-upon-a-time catastrophes, comparable to Noah's Flood. The early Radcliffe Observers were not in a position to recognize that, in addition to the daily vagaries of the weather of their years, there were also subtle long term trends that had long been in operation and would continue into the future.

1879-97 sixth Radcliffe Observer, Edward James Stone

After Main's death his successor, also appointed on the strong recommendation of the Astronomer Royal, was Edward Stone (1831-97). Formerly First Assistant at Greenwich, Stone was in 1878 the Astronomer at the Government's Observatory at the Cape of Good Hope in South Africa.

Before Stone could return to take up his new post in 1879 new standard thermometers, borrowed from the Meteoro-logical Office, were exposed from December 1878 in a newly erected double-louvred Stevenson stand over grass on the south lawn about 30 feet from the Observatory building. The height of the thermometer bulbs was initially five feet above ground level. In September 1885 this height was reduced by Stone to the standard four feet.

A Beckley self-registering 11.2 inch diameter rain gauge, lent by the Meteorological Office, had been installed on the north lawn of the Observatory in 1877 at a height known to be 208 feet above sea level and only some 5 feet distant from the Glaisher 8 inch gauge. After a period of calibration against the Glaisher gauge, the Beckley was brought into use early in the 1880s as the principal gauge for compiling the published tables. Its collections form the record of rainfall up to 1924, and it continued in subordinate use until 1963, with a short spell of relocation on the south lawn from 1935 to 1939. The scale of the Beckley enabled it to be read from midnight to midnight, which was convenient in some ways but gave rise to discordance with other gauges read at 8 a.m. or noon.

Stone alerted the Trustees in his first annual report to the fact that over the previous 30 years the equipment of the Radcliffe Observatory had fallen behind more advanced equipment introduced in observatories elsewhere. Specifically as regards meteorology he reported that the photographic records were becoming defective, something Main had already noted.

Although the Trustees could not afford expensive new astronomical instruments, improvements were made almost immediately in the meteorological instrumentation, with little expense to the Trustees. In 1880 a self-registering photographic barograph, a dry bulb thermograph and a wet bulb thermograph were installed and brought into use, comparable to the 1854 set of Radcliffe instruments but this time borrowed from the Meteorological Office and 'of the usual Kew type'.

Four Hicks thermometers were used on the thermographs. All four were placed within the same screen attached to the north wall of the observatory. One thermometer functioned as dry bulb and one as wet bulb, and the other two — standards thought to suffer no index errors — were read by eye three times a day as a check on the assumed scale value of the ordinates of the photographic curves. These new instruments gave thoroughly reliable results and were easier to read and calibrate than the traces of the ageing and deteriorating 1854 photographic instruments.

The instruments themselves remained in use until 1924 and readings were recorded although the reduced results were not published after 1905. Traces of the great storm of 24 October 1882 were sent to the Trustees; and displays illustrating traces for fine days in different months were sent to photographic exhibitions in London and Glasgow in 1896 and 1897.

Before his death in May 1897, and as something of an initiative, Stone ordered five or six 'underground' platinum resistance thermometers for the Observatory. However, he did not live to bring them into use. Glass thermometers are sufficiently robust when the thermometer is exposed in a Stevenson screen or other protected environment. For taking temperatures at different depths in the soil, robust electrical resistance thermometers make use of the fact that the electrical resistance of certain materials such as platinum varies with temperature.

In temperate climates the exact measurement of soil temperatures at different depths has some limited potential uses for farmers and construction engineers but Stone's initiative was probably motivated primarily by his spirit of scientific enquiry since little was known at the time about subsurface temperatures and the feedback effects this might have on the atmosphere and so the weather.

1897-1923 seventh Radcliffe Observer, Arthur Alcock Rambaut

Stone had found no option for renewing the obsolete astronomical instruments. The principal achievement of his successor Arthur Rambaut (1859-1923), Royal Astronomer for Ireland from 1892 to 1897, was to persuade the Trustees to refurbish the Observatory completely and re-equip it with a world-class photographic telescope, the 'Great Equatorial' telescope of 1903.

In extension of the Observatory's meteorological work, Rambaut first supervised the installation in 1898 of all but one of the new 'underground' platinum resistance thermometers purchased by Stone, in undisturbed gravel beneath the grass of the south lawn, within a few feet of the Stevenson screen. The purpose of these was to obtain readings of subsurface temperatures at depths of from six inches to ten feet. The remaining platinum resistance thermometer was placed in the observing room with the mercury thermometers as a check. Two Symons type (glass) earth thermometers were also suspended in prepared cavities at different depths. Very full results of the findings were eventually published in the 1911-15 volume of Radcliffe *Results*.[22] In 1878 few other observatories had begun making such observations, although such observations are now standard.

Observation of sub-surface soil temperatures at different places and in different soils has facilitated the calculation of terrestrial absorption of solar energy – which differs markedly from oceanic absorption of solar energy – and so has led to a greater understanding of heat exchanges between atmosphere and lithosphere, and of the implications of this for weather generation.

In 1908 Rambaut rationalized the location of the meteorological instruments within a new enclosure on the south lawn (details below, under *Locations*). In 1923 a Stevenson screen of a modern standard pattern was erected in the south lawn enclosure, close to and in place of the existing double-louvred Stevenson 'stand'. The thermometers from the old 'stand' or screen were transferred to the new screen. Later comparisons showed that the ventilation in the old screen had been defective, leading to a narrower range of readings than that obtained in the new screen. Readings from 1878 to 1923 were accordingly reduced to the standard of the new screen and the new results published by Rambaut's successor in the 1926-30 *Results* volume.

Through no fault of Rambaut, the status and importance of the Radcliffe Observatory as a source of meteorological observations was already declining in relative terms. More and more meteorological stations were making detailed observations; and reporting was becoming centralized, throughout Europe and in this country.

In 1854 a Meteorological Department had been set up within the Board of Trade under Captain FitzRoy, of *Beagle* fame. Following his premature death in 1865 official responsibility for meteorology was transferred in 1867 to a committee of the Royal Society under the chairmanship of Sir Edward Sabine. In 1877 responsibility was transferred once more, this time to a governmental Meteorological Council with R. H. Scott as Secretary. By way of a Meteorological Commission that body ultimately developed into the Meteorological Office.

The Radcliffe Observers co-operated readily with Committee, Council, Commission and Office. From around 1878 the Radcliffe Observatory adopted standard instruments borrowed from the Meteorological Office (or its predecessors under whatever name), to the financial relief of the Trustees; and the Observers followed procedures recommended by that Office. In the period 1873–1913 the Radcliffe Observatory was a 'Telegraphic Station', telegraphing observations daily to the Meteorological Office for use in its daily weather report.

The Meteorological Office with its increasingly numerous reporting stations continued to expand the scope of its activities. The Radcliffe Observatory (not under direct supervision) was therefore reduced in status in 1916 from a synoptic station, a key station (of which there were seven originally) providing observations taken into account in the formulation of the Meteorological Office daily weather report. The Radcliffe Observatory was regraded in 1916 as a climatological station, one of a dense network of smaller stations which provided more detailed if less immediate regional coverage, with the long term study of regional climates in mind. Telegraphic reporting from the Radcliffe Observatory was discontinued from 1 January 1914, and daily reporting by immediate post from 1916.

1924-35 eighth and last Radcliffe Observer to observe in Oxford, Harold Knox-Shaw

A former Director of the Meteorological Service of Egypt and the Sudan, where he was considered to have made valuable contributions to meteorology in connection with the study of solar radiation, Harold Knox-Shaw (1885-1970) was the last Radcliffe Observer to work in Oxford and the first in Pretoria, where he continued as Radcliffe Observer until 1950, having been largely responsible for the transfer of the Observatory to South Africa.

The Meteorological Office with its increasingly numerous subordinate reporting stations was continuing to expand the scope of its activities when Knox-Shaw was appointed. Unsurprisingly, eye-observations at the Radcliffe Observatory were reduced to once per day, at 9 a.m., in 1924.

At the end of 1924 the photographic barograph and the thermograph with its standard Hicks thermometers were returned to the Meteorological Office. A Short and Mason bi-metallic thermograph was brought into use at the beginning of 1925, situated in a Stevenson screen. For his main rain gauge Knox-Shaw reverted in 1925 to the 8 inch Glaisher gauge on the north lawn that had been in use there from 1877. This gauge was recognized as the Observatory's standard instrument.

In the meteorological field, Knox-Shaw's principal achievement before he left for South Africa was the publication of valuable, corrected results for the Observatory for the period from 1881 to 1930, with some results corrected back to 1815. Despite all the pressures upon him as a consequence since

1929 of the pending move to South Africa, Knox-Shaw was fully aware of the long term value for future climatic studies of the Radcliffe Observatory's long continuous meteorological observations. He recognized also that there had been a wide range of instruments in use over the previous century and more, and that some of these instruments had been exposed in different locations and with different screening at different times, so leading to doubts about their calibration and the reliability of results. With the assistance of his indefatigable assistant J. G. Balk he examined closely all the earlier records. Where it seemed possible to make reliable reductions to a common standard, this was done.

In the Appendix to Volume LV for 1926-30 of the *Radcliffe Meteorological Results*, revised tables of results were published of all the main weather elements from 1881 to 1930, while results for annual rainfall and dry-bulb temperatures were given from 1815 to 1930. The results published in this Appendix are now generally taken to supersede the earlier published values. Certainly they conform to a uniform standard as nearly as can usefully be achieved.

The Radcliffe Meteorological Station 1935-2000

Following the departure of the Radcliffe Observers to Pretoria, direction of the Radcliffe Meteorological Station was transferred to Oxford University and delegated to the School of Geography. The first Director, from 1935 to 1950, was W. G. Kendrew, a Fellow of St Catherine's College. Thereafter the Directors of the Meteorological Station have all been Fellows of Keble College. The Directors have all owed their primary tutorial responsibilities to their own College and their lecturing and research allegiance primarily to the University, more specifically to the School of Geography. For all of them the meteorological work of the Radcliffe has been a peripheral, if important, part of their duties.

None of them has been resident or worked from offices at the Radcliffe site. Most of the day to day observations have been undertaken by meteorological observers recruited from the ranks of postgraduate students at the School of Geography, and trained, in part, on courses at the Training School of the Meteorological Office.

The Radcliffe meteorological work began almost a century before any governmental meteorological service for the whole country was set up. Its early reports were eagerly sought by interested observers in scores of overseas countries and by 1899 the Radcliffe Observer was presenting annual Results volumes to over 120 institutions and individual meteorologists in Australia, Canada, South Africa, China, Japan, the United States of America, Latin America and almost all the major countries of Europe.

That situation no longer holds. Most developed countries have set up their own well organized meteorological services to which individual observatories and weather stations such as the Radcliffe send in their observations to be collated with other observations on a national basis.

For these reasons the meteorological work in Oxford has concentrated in recent years on maintaining the Radcliffe station in a good state of repair, bringing into use new instruments and equipment as appropriate, and sending in the carefully made observations promptly to the Meteorological Office in the prescribed form.

None the less the three longest serving Directors of the Meteorological Station are entitled to a brief mention here. Drawing on the Radcliffe record Kendrew, who later became first Director, wrote an excellent short account of the climate of the Oxford district in *The Natural History of the Oxford District*, published for the 1926 meeting in Oxford of the British Association.[23] His books *The Climates of the Continents*, and *Climatology* ran into many editions and were for long standard

textbooks. As Director he prepared the 1935-9 volume of *Radcliffe Results* before being obliged to leave Oxford on war service. There is a short published biography of Kendrew.[24]

C. G. Smith was Director of the Radcliffe Meteorological Station from 1950 to 1987. Like Kendrew he was a descriptive climatologist. As Station Director, Smith continued to insist on meticulous observation and recording of results. At one point as an economy measure the head of the School of Geography, Professor E. W. Gilbert, proposed that the School should seek to relinquish its responsibilities for maintaining the Radcliffe meteorological record. Smith argued vigorously and successfully that the School of Geography had an enduring obligation to maintain this uniquely valuable record for the foreseeable future. Smith used the Radcliffe record as a basis for a 1954 paper on Oxford's climate[25] and thereafter for a series of fifteen or so papers on specific types of weather experienced in Oxford: winters, cold winters, summers, temperatures, storms and the like.[26]

Smith was also responsible for achieving the removal of an unsightly wooden structure from the top of the tower (Plate 38, p. 60). It had at one stage been built to house a barometer and other instruments but these had outlived their usefulness. In 1976 reporting to the Meteorological Office was computerized.

The third long-serving Director, from 1987 to 1996, was T. P. Burt. It was in his time that the Campbell Automatic Weather Station was installed and brought into use. Burt continued the practice of contributing annual accounts of the weather at Oxford to the *British Journal of Meteorology*.

The fourth and fifth Directors served only briefly before moving on to other responsibilities, and the sixth was appointed too shortly before the closing date of this account for any assessment to be appropriate.

No major changes were introduced in the

Table 5.1 Rain gauge locations at the Radcliffe Observatory

	Dates	No. of years	Gauge from which main results were formulated, with its location
1	1767–93	27	New College Lane
2	1794–1814	21	Radcliffe Observatory site
3	1815–52	38	12" gauge at 22' on east parapet
4	1853–61	9	10" gauge on south lawn
5	1862–77	16	10" gauge on north lawn
6	1878–81	4	8" Glaisher on north lawn. Long term standard
7	1882–1924	43	11.2" Beckley self-registering, on north lawn
8	1925–34	10	8" Glaisher on north lawn
9	1935–9	5	8" Glaisher on south lawn
10	1940–63	24	8" Glaisher on north lawn
11	1964–2000	37	5" standard Met.Office gauge on north lawn

period 1996 to 2000 but instruments, borrowed from the Meteorological Office, have continued to be upgraded and replaced as necessary and full sets of observations both from the Campbell Automatic Weather Station and from the School of Geography Meteorological Observers are sent in promptly to the Meteorological Office. The eye-read values continue for the present to be regarded as the standard. It is intended that when the automatic station has been going for a sufficient number of years a detailed comparison will be made between the two sets of results.

Locations and exposures of the meteorological instruments and publication of the results

The locations and exposures of the various meteorological instruments changed on many occasions over some two centuries but never for whimsical reasons. The instruments too changed from time to time as old instruments wore out, or new and better designs were brought in. When changes had to be effected serious attempts were made to arrange overlapping periods of two or more years in which the old exposure and the new could be monitored with matching instruments in order to establish reliable conversion coefficients between the two sites, or the two instruments. Published results were frequently recalculated to reduce earlier results to the new accepted standard.

Rainfall

Precipitation, for example, forming the Radcliffe's longest continuous record, was collected in a range of gauges in no fewer than eleven locations (see Table 5.1).

The principal rain gauge was exposed on the parapet from 1815 because it was expected that this would give the most reliable results. Articles in *The Philosophical Magazine* of 1823,[27] and the *Comptes Rendus* of 1851,[28] and no doubt other authorities around this time, recommended for a variety of reasons that all rain gauges should be sited at ground level as soon as possible. The Radcliffe fell into line from 1853, siting a 10 inch gauge on the south lawn. Early switches of rain gauge between north and south lawns were made in the hope of obtaining 'better exposure' or 'less-sheltered conditions'. Later switches between the 8 inch Glaisher (eye-read) rain gauge and the Beckley (self-recording) gauge, both exposed at ground level, were made primarily for convenience in times of observation.

For comparative purposes the Observatory continued until 1879 to collect precipitation in subordinate gauges at a range of heights – from the lawns, the parapet, the wall of the kitchen garden and the top of the tower. The diminution in catch at increasing height was recorded in an article on meteorology in the eleventh, 1911, edition of the *Encyclopedia Britannica*.

Atmospheric pressure

Changes of location of the eye-read barometer have been much less frequent. The Bird Barometer was used until 1838. Thereafter the only main instrument in use has been the Newman, situated two feet above floor level in the Observatory building at a cistern height of 212 feet above Ordnance Datum. With a few short intervals for servicing, during which a Jones and other barometers deputized, the Newman has remained the standard until today. It is still as accurate as ever, having been checked many times against Kew standards.

The Ronald barograph of 1854 was situated in a small north room in the main building. The 1880 barograph was mounted in a room between the transit circle and mural circle rooms.

Temperature recording

The main eye-read thermometers have been frequently replaced, and were resited several times in search of better exposure. They have always been purchased from reliable makers and checked frequently against Kew standards, as well as having freezing points checked almost annually in melting snow. Initially exposed unscreened on the north wall of the Observatory, they were subsequently exposed from 1849 to 1878 in a home-made wooden penthouse some six feet from the north wall

In December 1878 new thermometers, lent by the Meteorological Office, were exposed over grass in a Stevenson stand on the south lawn at a natural elevation of 206 feet. In 1908 this stand, protected by a new railed enclosure, 30 feet by 12 feet in size, was moved five feet further south, to be some 38 feet from

the lower part of the Observatory building and 46 feet from the 100 foot tower. There had been fears that the recorded temperatures from the 1878 site might have been affected by the proximity of the building or a gravel path. The effect on thermometer readings was found to be insensible. The underground thermometers appear to have been included within the new 1908 enclosure but were apparently not moved or disturbed.

In January 1923 a new Stevenson screen was erected within the same 30 feet by 12 feet railed enclosure, and the instruments transferred to it. This screen turned out to have improved ventilation, necessitating a recalculation of results from thermometers in the earlier stand. On 1 January 1935 the standard instruments were moved some 60 feet, to a new Stevenson screen in a new enclosure, 30 feet by 18 feet in size, in the middle of the south lawn. At this time both the 8 inch Glaisher rain gauge and the Beckley self-recording gauge from the north lawn were resited in the south lawn enclosure, as were the grass minimum thermometers.

In the period 1930 to 1936 a further Stevenson screen with thermometers was temporarily maintained on the north lawn to ascertain what effect, if any, on temperature readings would result from the proposed construction of new hospital buildings 100 feet from the screen on the south lawn.

However, the arrival of war in 1939 and the need to allow for the possible rapid expansion of the Radcliffe Infirmary on to the Observatory's south lawn forced a return of the meteorological instruments to the north lawn in September 1939, where they have remained ever since, at a natural elevation of 208 feet (Plate 53, p. 102). At the request of the Nuffield Institute for Medical Research (the then owners of the building) they were sited in a smaller 24 foot by 12 foot enclosure.

The positioning of all the varying maximum and minimum thermometers and the sky and solar radiation thermometers in use since the 1850s changed many times over the years, and for good reason, but need not be detailed here.

The thermograph and hygrograph of 1854, located in a north-facing window, initially had only their bulbs exposed to the outside air but had to be re-positioned in 1856 with the whole of their lengths exposed to the atmosphere. The Hicks photographic thermograph of 1880 was placed in a screen attached to the north wall of the main Observatory building.

Anemographs

Until 1856, estimates of wind direction and horizontal movement, in miles per day, were made exclusively by eye. Thereafter they were checked against readings of an Adie self-registering anemograph exposed initially at 22 feet. Readings appeared too low by Kew standards and in 1858 the Adie was raised to the top of the tower at 110 feet. This gave readings much more in line with those of Kew. Until 1883 the values for wind speed were given on a scale of zero (calm) to six (storm) and mean directions given by 16 compass points. From 1 January 1884, in line with Meteorological Office recommendations, the Observatory adopted the Beaufort 0-12 scale, estimated with the aid of the anemometer at 110 feet. From 1918 directions were shown in degrees counted clockwise from north, and speeds recorded in knots (nautical miles per hour) at the height of the anemograph.

Campbell weather station

In May 1994 a Campbell Automatic Weather Station was installed on the north lawn within the railed enclosure in replacement of a Stevenson screen containing the thermograph that had been used up till then. This station runs for sixteen days without attention. It is read and reset twice a month.

Relations with the Meteorological Office

The present situation is that the Meteoro-logical Office lends instruments to the Radcliffe Meteorological Station and undertakes calibration of the instruments in return for the Station's services in making its observations and communicating its results. Instruments are maintained, refurbished or replaced with like instruments by the Meteorological Office as necessary. Radcliffe Station Observers are sent on courses to the Meteorological Office Training School as appropriate. As part of the agreement the Meteorological Office inspects the Radcliffe Station on a regular basis. Thus far the Station has obtained a good report.

Timings

From 1815 to 1924 three readings were made every day of all the principal barometric and thermometric instruments, and after 1856, of the anemometers also. Cloud amounts were also estimated at the same times. For most of this time up to 1888, readings were made at 10 a.m., 2 p.m. and 10 p.m. Times were adjusted slightly in 1889 and 1915, the last adjustment in response to non-availability of staff during the 1914-19 war. Rain gauges were read once per day, usually at 10 a.m. or some other hour in the morning. However the Beckley self-registering gauge tended to be read at noon and scaled from midnight to midnight. This gave logically correct readings for each civil day but had the disadvantage of differing from the eye-read gauges when rain fell at night.

Since 1925, and up to the present, these main instruments have continued to be read once per day, in recent years at 9 a.m., in parallel with readings of the Campbell automatic weather station in order to provide continuity of instrumentation and record.

The reckoning of time has varied over the years. Oxford local time was used until 1879, Greenwich mean time thereafter. Days have normally followed civil reckoning and been counted from midnight to midnight but from 1 January 1857 to 31 December 1888

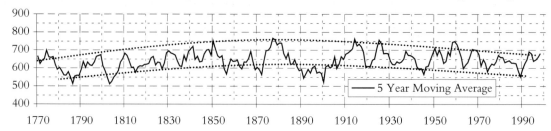

Fig.5.1   Annual Precipitation (mm) 1770-2000:   5 Year Moving Average

the astronomical day, midday to midday, was used for meteorological reckoning also.

Publication of results

Although there are long continuous records from other observatories in the British Isles, notably at Greenwich, Kew, Durham and Armagh, the Radcliffe Observatory in Oxford possesses the longest continuous series of temperature and rainfall records in Britain for one site. Daily records for these are continuous from 1 January 1815. Records for all the main meteorological elements are continuous from 1828 and available in published form from 1853.

Publication of the Radcliffe Observatory's Results before 1853 was patchy and unsystematic; however, Robertson and Rigaud had minor publishing successes. From 1853 to 1935 comprehensive Radcliffe Observatory Meteorological Results were published together with the astronomical Results in volumes that for the most part appeared annually under such titles as *Astronomical and Meteorological Observations made at the Radcliffe Observatory, Oxford* (titles vary).[32] Offprints of the meteorological results are also available for the whole of this period. Separate publication of Radcliffe Meteorological Results terminated after the 1935-9 volume, the Director being absent on war service. Thereafter one has to look to Meteorological Office and other publications for the Oxford results. Fuller details have been published elsewhere.[33]

Changes in Oxford's weather 1767-2000

Except in a very limited, local way South Central England does not generate its own weather patterns. The weather recorded at the Radcliffe Observatory is the weather of air masses and air streams reaching us from elsewhere. Consequently, the principal long term value of the Radcliffe meteorological record, taken in conjunction with other long term records from observatories such as Greenwich, Kew and Durham, is that it gives a rather precise history of the weather of southern Britain over the last two centuries or so, for most of that time on a daily basis. The section that follows will paint a broad-brush picture of the main changes in the main climatic elements over the period.

Limitations of space preclude reference to freak wind or rain storms or other unusual weather events which by their nature tend to be highly localized.

Interpreted cautiously the long term meteorological records have the potential to contribute to our ability to make certain predictions concerning future weather trends in this country. However, there are innumerable variables and many gaps in current knowledge. The authors of the UK Climatic Impacts Programme offer no more than a range of possible scenarios for climate-change but they do not offer predictions. [34]

Precipitation

Long term mean (LTM) annual precipitation for the whole period has been roughly 642

Table 5.2 Range of precipitation

Annual fall (mm)	>799	750-99	700-49	650-99	600-49	550-99	500-49	450-99	<450	1767-2000
No. of years	18	20	24	50	35	40	25	13	9	234
Annual mean	864	779	725	677	628	577	525	477	411	643
Standard deviation	59.2	15.0	14.9	14.8	14.2	14.0	10.7	12.7	27.1	112.3

millimetres or 25 inches. Hundred year means for the nineteenth and twentieth centuries both evaluate to within three or four millimetres of the LTM, suggesting at first sight that Oxford's annual rainfall has been rather constant over the last 234 years. It has not; there is a distinct hump in the middle of the period (see Figure 5.1).

In Oxford, at the start and end of this 234-year record, rainfall has been relatively low, averaging 600 millimetres or less for several years at a time. In the middle years of the period it has peaked on several occasions at averages of well over 700 millimetres for five or more years at a stretch (see Table 5.2).

Roughly three years out of four, precipitation falls within the range 500-750 millimetres.

Throughout the period there is considerable variation from year to year. The mean absolute difference between consecutive years is 127 millimetres, and many consecutive years differ by much more. Extreme years are more likely to be sandwiched between normal years than to appear as the culmination of an extreme period. Rapid variation between years is perhaps not unexpected since in many cases it seems to reflect a modest fluctuation in timing rather than a major fluctuation in magnitude. For example November and December of 1851 were both exceptionally dry, together registering about 70 millimetres below average, whereas January of 1852 was the wettest January on record at 139 millimetres, registering about 85 millimetres above the mean of the month. It is difficult to resist the conclusion that the rain expected in

November and December fell as usual but, for some reason, several weeks late.

Annual and seasonal rainfall has usually been adequate for stock and cereal farming though some crops may benefit from irrigation, or need it. There have been winter floods, some of them originating from human interference with natural drainage patterns; also there have been several periods of rainfall deficit amounting eventually to drought. There were two 7-year periods of water shortage at the end of the eighteenth and beginning of the nineteenth century and there have been four 4-year droughts since 1767, the last of them in the early 1990s.

Snow cover has been variable, and since 1963 has diminished sharply. There are doubts about the methods of observation used at the Observatory in the early years before observational methods were standardized nationally by the Meteorological Office. However, M. C. Jackson writing in 1978 found the median number of days per winter with snow lying in Oxford to be 6.5 for the 30 years 1911-40 and 11.5 for the 30 years 1941-70. 'Once-in-5-year snowy winters' numbered 13 and 20 for the two periods, a finding that raises questions about the definition and calculation of what constitutes a generally acceptable 'once-in-5-year snowy winter'.

Pattern or not in precipitation received?
It is easier to discern trends when the wilder swings of annual values are eliminated by using moving averages. There is always some danger that an ill-chosen moving average may

Fig. 5.2 Seasonal Precipitation (mm) 1770-2000: 5 Year Moving Averages

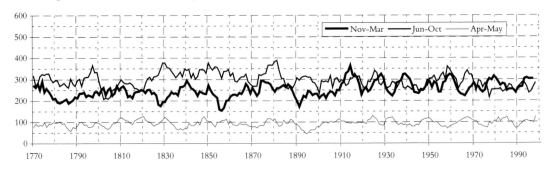

suggest the existence of a trend that is in part an artefact of the averaging period chosen, and not a genuine weather phenomenon. However, in this case 5-year moving averages do not appear to lead to serious error.

Viewed as a 5-year moving average, the graph for rainfall at Oxford since 1770 (see Figure 5.1) may be viewed as forming a shallow arch rising in the middle to a major rainfall peak around 1875-85. Immediately before and after this major peak of wet weather lie 20-year periods of much drier weather, the second of these coinciding in part with the coldest period of weather experienced by Oxford since the 1690s. The 20 years 1830-50 and the 20 years 1950-70 are both marked by three peaks of rainfall at intervals of ten years; and there are further periods of 20 years or so (1800-23 and 1915-37), when three peaks of rainfall are found at around ten year intervals. This distribution could be, but probably is not, random.

Seasonality of rainfall

The seasonality of rainfall has changed considerably over the 234 years. Figure 5.2, plotted as a 5-year moving average, brings out several features. April and May changed least over the period, together averaging close to 100 millimetres per year throughout.

The dry summers and autumns (June to October) of the period 1800-20 appear anomalous with many exceptionally dry

months and few unusually wet months. Except for this anomalous period, in the 110 years 1770-1880 the five summer and autumn months June to October were, in total, consistently wet, precipitation averaging over 300 millimetres annually. For most of this time these months produced an excess of annual rainfall over the winter five months (November to March) that often reached or exceeded 100 millimetres in magnitude. The winter five months fluctuated unpredictably, mainly in the range 150-250 millimetres.

There is little sign of periodic or cyclic pattern in either summer or winter rainfall in the period 1770-1910. However, it was frequently the case for a few years at a time that, if one of these two seasons was wetter than usual, the other was drier than usual.

Commencing at around 1880, summers rather quickly became drier by about 50 millimetres; soon afterwards the winter five months appear rather quickly to have become wetter, by 50 millimetres or more. Winter rainfall before 1890 tended to come in 25-35 year waves of wet weather, interrupted by short lived dips where for a few years the annual rainfall dropped to as little as 150 millimetres. After 1910 rainfall for both summer and winter five months tended to oscillate narrowly, over a 10- or 11-year period, between 225 millimetres and 325 millimetres.

Further examination of the situation

Fig. 5.3 Persistently wet months 1707-1998

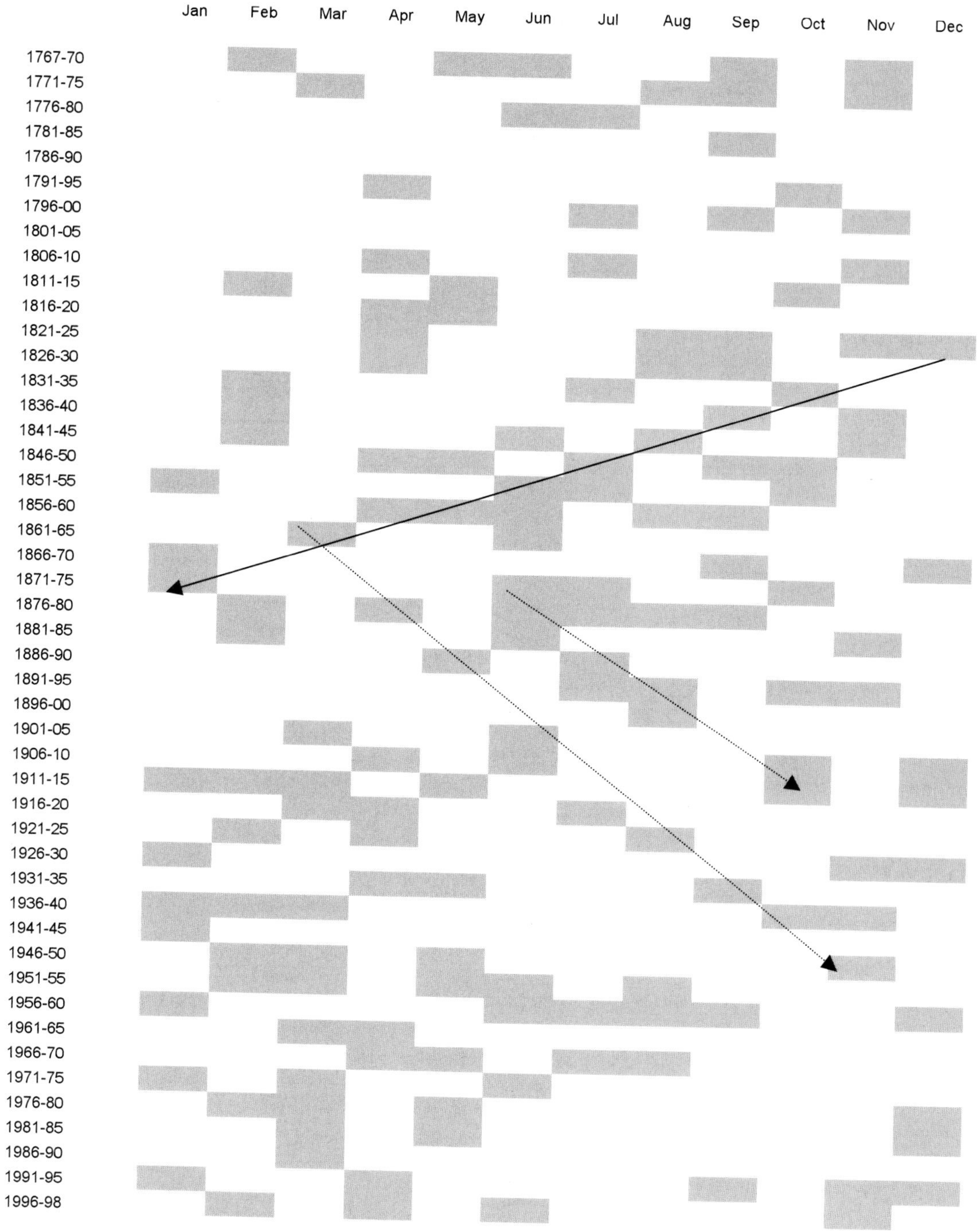

Shaded blocks indicate months in each pentad with precipitation persistently
15% or more above the Long Term Means of the months in question.

Table 5.3 Long term mean seasonal and annual screen temperatures

Winter (Dec–Feb)	Spring (Mar–May)	Summer (Jun–Aug)	Autumn (Sep–Nov)	Annual
4.1	8.6	16.0	10.1	9.6

Table 5.4 Ranges of temperature in degrees Celsius
(mean maximum for the months less mean minimum)

	Winter	Spring	Summer	Autumn	Annual
Greatest	6.9 (1891)	13.0 (1893)	12.5 (1976)	9.8 (1921)	9.4 (1893)
Least	4.3 (1972)	6.6 (1981)	7.6 (1954)	5.5 (1968)	6.4 (1968)
Difference	2.6	6.4	4.9	4.3	3.0

Table 5.5 Maximum, mean and minimum long term monthly means
for screen air temperatures

Jan	Feb	Mar	Apr	May	Jun	Jul	Aug	Sep	Oct	Nov	Dec
6.7	7.3	9.9	13.0	16.7	19.7	21.6	21.1	18.5	14.0	9.7	7.4
3.6	4.1	5.7	8.2	11.5	14.8	16.5	16.1	13.6	10.0	6.4	4.5
1.4	1.3	2.4	4.2	7.1	10.1	12.2	11.9	9.7	6.7	3.7	2.1

suggests that the apparent change of regime in the period 1880-1910 was not quite so sudden or so unexpected as it appears from Figure 5.2.

Careful analysis of the Radcliffe rainfall records indicates that in any pentad (period of five consecutive years) since the early 1800s, and probably since the 1770s, monthly rainfall, when averaged over those five years, shows some tendency to peak at 20-40 per cent above the long term mean of the month for two, three or four consecutive months. Sometimes there are two blocks of two or more consecutive wet months in each pentad.

Interestingly, these two-to-three-month blocks of wet weather appear to backtrack through the year over durations of 50-100 years (Figure 5.3).

Thus, one surge of wetter-than-usual weather can perhaps be traced from November-December in the pentad 1821-5, through late summer around 1840, to early summer in 1851-5, and on to January and February by 1866-70. Another 1-or-2-month

block of wet weather, slow moving but intense, can perhaps be descried, backtracking from November in 1836-45 to July by 1886-95, to March by 1911-20, to January by 1936-45, and to December by 1976-85.

It is tempting to hypothesize that these blocks of unusually wet weather are caused by periodic fluctuations in the relative strengths of three main weather generators – Azores and North Polar High Pressure cells and the Icelandic Low – and are not simply random. More work would be needed to establish if this were so, and why. If this is a genuine trend then we may expect the wetter weather now experienced in December to drift in time towards late autumn and then early autumn, with more frequent and greater snowfall returning in winter months, perhaps by around 2020-30.

Annual, seasonal and monthly temperatures
Tables 5.3-5.5 above show that mean annual temperatures over the period 1815-2000 have

Fig. 5.4 Annual Mean Air Temperature, °C, 1815-2000
with 19 Year Moving Average

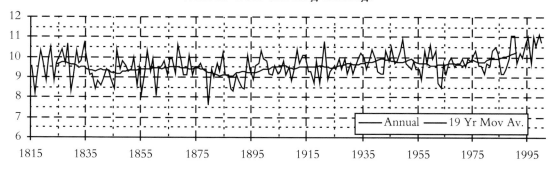

been less subject to wild fluctuation than rainfall values.

Long term temperature trends

Annual values, inspected at a range of 3, 5, 7, 11 and 19 year moving averages, emphasize different features of the record but are not at odds with one another. Taking whichever moving average is most convenient, it is clear that mean annual screen temperatures in the middle 1820s and 1830s had been close to 10 degrees Celsius and had fallen to a little below 9 degrees Celsius by 1840 (see Figure 5.4).

There was a 45-50 year wave of warmer weather cresting at close to 10 degrees Celsius around 1868 and falling again to about 8.7 degrees Celsius in the late 1880s and early 1890s. These years are the coldest years of the record.

There was a steep rise of nearly a degree and a half during the 1890s, almost comparable with the very sharp rise in temperature two centuries before in central and southern England, from the late 1690s to 1710, that brought the country out of the last 'Little Ice Age'. Following the sudden rises in temperature in the 1690s and again in the 1890s, temperatures have continued to fluctuate. Yet in neither case was there a significant reversion to colder weather. Each rise seems to represent a step to a new temperature plateau, some one and a half Celsius degrees higher than before.

Although the rise from 1890 flattened out somewhat after 1899, temperatures continued to rise steadily until the end of the 1940s by which time the 5-year average mean temperature was again 10 degrees Celsius or above. Since then there have been swings up and down at about 10 year intervals. Since 1963 the trend of these swings has been sharply upward. Five-year average annual mean temperatures rose above 10 degrees Celsius in the 1980s and topped 10.5 degrees Celsius in the late 1990s. Some predict that temperatures will continue to rise inexorably to 2030, 2080 and beyond.

The rise in mean temperatures after 1890 is to a large extent a reflection of a substantial increase in mean minimum temperatures. In the late 1880s and early 1890s the mean minimum temperature for the winter six months (November to April) was steadily below 2 degrees Celsius. It is now nearly 4 degrees Celsius. Following the rise in the 1890s, and until 1963, the winter minimum was relatively steady at between 2.5 degrees Celsius and 3 degrees Celsius. Since 1963 (an exceptionally cold winter caused chiefly by a stationary blocking anticyclone west of Norway that forced depressions far north or south of their normal latitudes) there has been no really cold winter in south central England. The four highest minimum temperature values in the whole record for the winter six months have all occurred since 1989.

In the summer six months also (May to October) it is the rise in the mean minimum temperature that has helped bring about a change in Britain's weather. Before 1990 maximum temperatures, winter or summer, had fluctuated within a narrow range and shown no long term upward trend. Indeed from the 1950s until the end of the 1980s summer maxima have in general been below the level of the years 1900-50.

On the other hand summer minimum temperatures have crept up, though not so sharply as winter minima. For most of the period 1890-1930 summer minimum temperatures had been lower than winter maximum temperatures, by half a degree or so. Since 1930 summer minima have been higher, by half a degree or so, than winter maxima.

Sunshine received

The deep dip in temperatures in the 1880s and the sharp rise in the 1980s can to some extent be explained by looking at the Radcliffe Observatory's record of bright sunshine received. The sunshine was recorded by a Campbell-Stokes glass sphere sunshine recorder at the top of the Observatory tower from 1880 at a height of approximately 105 feet above ground level; a similar instrument was situated on top of the University Engineering Science building at a height of 115 feet from 1976.

The number of hours of bright sunshine received over the course of the year declined in the 1880s from almost 1500 hours to below 1300 hours in 1890, the lowest point on the sunshine record. There was a quick recovery thereafter and for most of the next 80 years the hours recorded annually fluctuated between 1400 and 1600. Following a dip in the early 1980s to just below 1400 hours the sunshine received climbed quickly to two peaks of over 1700 hours in the 1990s.

Given that the output of the sun in the visible spectrum fluctuates very little over the time scales considered here, the number of hours of bright sunshine received would appear to depend primarily on local cloudiness, which in turn depends on the relative strengths of high and low pressure systems such as the Azores High and the Icelandic Low. Likely causes of change in the major pressure systems include secular changes in the temperature distribution of the waters of the Atlantic, comparable to – if more localized than – the El Niño Southern Oscillation of the Pacific. Understanding of a generating mechanism for this must await results from global climate models still under development.

Global warming of man's making has undoubtedly contributed to the rise to what are now the highest temperatures in historic times. However, natural factors are still important, probably predominant. Two rather noticeable dips in temperature in south central England that occurred in the 1950s and 1960s are not likely to have resulted from any slackening of industrial endeavour. Temperatures globally are still a degree or more below the summer and winter temperatures reached some 6,000 or 7,000 years ago, in the so-called 'Atlantic Optimum' period of warmer (and in many places, wetter) weather, when parts of the Sahara supported vegetation.

Outlook?

There are well-attested, if somewhat irregular, periodicities in the earth's climate and weather. One of these is a cycle of two hundred years or so, long-known in Western Europe and in China. From work undertaken by Soviet researchers at Vostok on the Antarctic plateau it now seems clear that this periodicity has been in existence for at least the last ten thousand years. It is presumably a function of variables in the operating of the solar system and may be presumed to continue for some time to come.

If weather patterns continue as before, (and they may not, irrespective of the complications introduced by industrial pollution and warming) we may find transient dips of one or more degrees Celsius in annual temperatures in the 2020s and again in the 2050s. We may expect rainfall in south central England to continue to decline until the 2020s before slowly increasing again. Rainfall peaks may move away from winter to autumn; winters may again become cold and may bring substantial snowfall by 2025. April may again bring sweet showers to soothe the droughts of March. Who knows? This is all speculative, but not highly improbable.

NOTES

1. Farnell, L. (1934) *An Oxonian Looks Back.* London, Hopkinson. 65-68.

2. *Comptes Rendus de l'Académie des Sciences* (January-June 1895) Gauthier-Villars et Fils Imprimeurs-Libraires, Paris. CXX: 731-3.

3. Brockliss, L. W. B (1997) The European University in the Age of Revolution, 1789-1850. In Brock, M. G. and Curthoys, M. C. (Ed.) *The History of the University of Oxford* Volume VI: *Nineteenth-Century Oxford*, Part 1. Clarendon Press, Oxford. 126

4. Simcock, A.V. (1984) *The Ashmolean Museum and Oxford Science 1683-1983.* Oxford Museum of the History of Science.

5. *Oxford Dictionary of National Biography* (2004). Oxford University Press, Oxford. 28: 169.

6. Ward, W. R. (1965) *Victorian Oxford.* London, Frank Cass & Co. Ltd. 8.

7. Wood, H. J. (1951) *Exploration and Discovery.* Hutchinson's University Library, London. 124-7.

8. Smith, C. G. (1985) Meteorological Observations at the Radcliffe Observatory, Oxford. *Bulletin of the Scientific Instrument Society.* 5: 11-13.

9. Craddock, J. M. and E. (1977) Rainfall at Oxford from 1767 to 1814, estimated from the records of Dr Thomas Hornsby and others. *Meteorological Magazine.* 107: 361-72.

10. Gunther, R. T. (1923) *Early Science in Oxford.* Oxford Historical Society Publications. Oxford. I: 323.

11. Cox, G. V. (1868) *Recollections of Oxford.* London, Macmillan. 135.

12. Ward (1965) 8.

13. Rigaud, S. P. (1835) Remarks on the proportionate quantities of rain at different seasons in Oxford. *Transactions of the Ashmolean Society*, 1: 5-19.

14. Details of the Metonic cycle may be found under 'Meton' in the Oxford Classical Dictionary.

15. Rigaud (1935).

16. Airy, G. B. (1851) On the relation of the direction of the wind to the age of the moon as inferred from observations made at the Royal Observatory, Greenwich, from 1840 November to 1847 December. *Phil. Trans. R. Soc. Lond.* 141.

17. Sabine, E. (1854) Letter, covering translation from German of a contribution from Professor Dove. *London and Edinburgh Philosophical Magazine*, 4th Series. 8: 294-301.

18. Main, R. (1874) *Report of the Radcliffe Observer to the Board of Trustees.* Privately printed by Hall & Stacey, Printers to the University. 5.

19. Main, R. (1875) *On the rainfall for 25 years (1851-1875) as observed at the Radcliffe Observatory, Oxford.* Read before the Ashmolean Society, 13 December 1875 and printed by order of the Society. Printers Hall and Stacy, printers to the University.

20. Buchan, A. (1871) *Introductory Textbook of Meteorology.* Edinburgh.

21. Main (1875) 6.

22. Radcliffe Observatory (1842-1937) (*Results of) Astronomical (and Meteorological) Observations Made at the Radcliffe Observatory in …1840 (1931/35).* (Titles vary) Oxford. I – LVI; Radcliffe Observatory (1855-1937) (*Results of) Meteorological Observations Made at the Radcliffe Observatory in …1853 (1931/35)* (Titles vary) Oxford. Being offprints from Volumes XIV – LVI.

23. Kendrew, W. G. (1926) Climate. In Walker, J. (Ed.) *The Natural History of the Oxford District.* Published for the British Association 1926 meeting. Oxford University Press, Oxford. 21-6.

24. Smith, C. G. (1997) Wilfrid George Kendrew. In *GEOGRAPHERS Biobibliographical Studies.* 17: 43-51.

25. Smith, C. G. (1954) Climate. In Martin, A. F. and Steel, R. W. (Eds.) *The Oxford Region*. Oxford University Press, Oxford. 37–49.

26. A full list of these may be found in Wallace, J. G. (1997). *Meteorological Observations at the Radcliffe Observatory Oxford: 1815-1995*. School of Geography Research Paper 53.

27. Tilloch, A. and Taylor, R. (Eds) (1823) *The Philosophical Magazine and Journal*. Printed by Richard Taylor, Shoe Lane, London. LXI: 321.

28. *Comptes Rendus de l'Académie des Sciences* (July–December 1851) Bachelier Imprimeur-Libraires, Paris. XXXIII: 602-4.

29. *Encyclopaedia Britannica* (1910-11) Cambridge University Press, Cambridge. 11th Edition. XVIII: 276.

30. Radcliffe Observatory (1842-1937).

31. Wallace (1997) 72-75.

32. Hulme, M. and Jenkins, G. I. (1998) *Climate Change Scenarios for the UK: Scientific Report*. UKCIP Technical Report 1, C. Climate Research Unit, University of East Anglia, Norwich.

Chapter 6

The Radcliffe Observatory and Medicine

Irvine Loudon and Terence Ryan

Part 1

The Background: Clinical Medicine in Oxford 1920-50

Irvine Loudon

One can think of the history of the Radcliffe Observatory as if it were a biography of an individual who was unusual in having three quite different occupations in a long life: first astronomy and meteorology, secondly medical research and finally a position as the centrepiece of an Oxford college. The importance of looking at the Observatory from this point of view is to emphasize that there was no inherent logic in these changes. The changes took place from purely accidental circumstances.

When the Radcliffe Trustees agreed to fund the building of the Observatory, a site was needed which was reasonably far from the centre of Oxford to avoid atmospheric pollution. It could have been anywhere in the outskirts of the city. The present site was chosen in 1770 when the Radcliffe Infirmary had just been opened, allowing the Radcliffe Trustees to turn their attention to their next project – the building of an observatory. Hearing of this, the fourth Duke of Marlborough, who had a passionate interest in astronomy, intervened by offering the gift of land adjacent to the Radcliffe Infirmary as a site for the Observatory. The offer was acceptable to Hornsby (see Chapter 1) who was the moving spirit behind the plan to build an observatory, and to the Radcliffe Trustees who would have to pay the bills.[1]

Although they were next door to each other, there was absolutely no connection between the Radcliffe Observatory and the Radcliffe Infirmary until the 1930s. If the Observatory had been built somewhere else in Oxford its history would have been different. So, to understand the connection between the Observatory and medicine we must look briefly at the story of clinical medicine in Oxford in the twentieth century.

Clinical medicine in Oxford before the 1930s

In Oxford, as in most universities in the UK and many Western countries, the teaching of medicine is divided into two stages – first, the pre-clinical stage consisting of medical sciences such as anatomy, physiology and biochemistry and secondly, the clinical stage which takes place in a teaching hospital.[2]

In most universities the pre-clinical departments and the teaching hospitals are closely linked in the same city. Until the outbreak of the Second World War, however, Oxford students had to go somewhere outside Oxford for their three years of clinical training because the Radcliffe Infirmary was not a teaching hospital.[3] This geographical separation of the basic medical sciences and clinical training occurred at only three universities in the UK: Oxford, Cambridge and St Andrews.

Before the mid-1930s, the Radcliffe Infirmary was a typical provincial hospital serving about a quarter of a million people. The standards and staff were those of a competent provincial hospital but no more than that; and there was certainly no inclination to do research.[4]

Although the Radcliffe Infirmary was, in effect, a provincial hospital in the same league as the infirmaries at Exeter, Gloucester, Hereford, Northampton, Shrewsbury or Winchester (all of which were founded in the second half of the eighteenth century) there was a difference. There were links, albeit weak ones, between the Radcliffe Infirmary and the University of Oxford.

The most obvious link was examinations for medical degrees. When students had completed their course of clinical training, they had to return to Oxford to take their final examination for the Oxford degree of BM BCh (Bachelor of Medicine and Bachelor of Surgery). Because this examination (which, in the 1930s was held twice a year) included the examination of out-patients and in-patients, it was always held at the Radcliffe Infirmary.[5]

There were other links between medicine and the University. Since 1546 Oxford has elected a series of Regius Professors of Medicine. By 2000 there had been thirty holders of this office. Throughout the eighteenth and nineteenth centuries, many Regius Professors of Medicine were nonentities who lived a quiet life of inactivity. This, however, was no longer true when Sir William Osler (1849-1919) was elected Regius Professor in 1904. Osler, a man of charm and energy, arrived in Oxford with a high reputation for teaching and clinical ability. He was probably the first Regius Professor to hold regular teaching rounds once or twice a week at the Radcliffe Infirmary, and it is said that his radiant and outgoing personality made his ward rounds memorable, although who attended these rounds is not clear.

Osler's successor was Sir Archibald Garrod (1857-1936) who held the post of Regius Professor from 1920-8. Garrod was a scientist of exceptional ability whose classic work, *Inborn Errors of Metabolism*, published in 1909, is said to mark the beginning of medical genetics.[6] Garrod also:

> … undertook teaching rounds once or twice a week at the Radcliffe Infirmary, and if they differed [from Osler's] it was that Garrod, though kindly and avuncular, did not possess Osler's easy charm, cheerfulness and irrepressible confidence. While Osler was the clinician and Garrod the scientist, both tried in their own, though small way, to begin the process of turning Oxford into a centre of medical science and research.[7]

They certainly tried, but persuading a university which was steeped in the humanities to accept clinical medicine as an academic discipline was a continual uphill struggle.

As recently as the 1930s Oxford University's attitude to medicine was one of indifference, if not hostility. In the 1920s, when the Department of Medicine was housed in cramped quarters in the University

Museum, Garrod wrote:

> Some of us believe that it would be highly desirable to establish in Oxford an organized, postgraduate clinic, in which some of our graduates, and other picked men, might pursue the study of scientific clinical Medicine ... [but] ... we see little prospect of a speedy realization of this project.[8]

The clearest indication of the University's indifference to medicine came when the University showed no interest in a proposal by the Rockefeller Foundation in 1927 to finance a postgraduate medical school in Oxford.[9] In fact, the offer was 'not so much turned down as totally ignored . . . the University then took very little interest in medical affairs'.[10] The money went instead to London to found the Postgraduate School of Medicine at Hammersmith.

The transformation of clinical medicine in Oxford

It is unlikely that anyone in the late 1920s foresaw the extent to which clinical medicine in Oxford would be transformed over the next decade; the use of the term 'transformation' is no exaggeration. It was not driven by any national plan respecting medical teaching and practice. The transformation in Oxford was essentially a local affair, initiated by a few people of whom the outstanding figures were Hugh Cairns (1896-1952) who became the first Nuffield Professor of Surgery; Sir Edward Farquhar Buzzard (1871-1945), Regius Professor of Medicine from 1928-43; Douglas Veale (1891-1973), the University Registrar;[11] and most of all William Morris (later Sir William Morris and then Lord Nuffield).[12] Before they had even met each other, Morris, Cairns and Farquhar Buzzard had, like Garrod, independently developed ideas about the possibility of creating some sort of postgraduate medical school in Oxford.

That the Radcliffe Observatory might be involved in these plans for the reform of medicine in Oxford occurred to Sir William Morris as early as 1927 when the idea of moving the astronomers to South Africa was taking shape. With the ultimate reform of Oxford medicine in mind, Nuffield decided to buy the Observatory site. He made an offer of £100,000 to the Radcliffe Trustees. The Trustees, who had rejected other plans for the future of the building, could hardly refuse such a sum. The sale was completed on the 26th July 1929 although it was agreed that the Observatory would continue with astronomical work until 1934.[13]

Nuffield bought the Observatory in 1929 because he wanted the whole site for the future expansion of the Radcliffe Infirmary. It is doubtful at this early stage that he foresaw the Observatory specifically as a centre for medical research. On the 5th March 1930, however, a proposal was made to the Medicine Board that the Observatory should be used for medical research. Formal plans to that effect were drawn up by the University in Hilary Term 1934 when the University guaranteed the sum of £1,000 per annum and the Board of the Faculty of Medicine agreed that a recent bequest of £30,000 from the late Mrs Theodore Williams should be used for endowment.

Thus some funding was obtained which, although quite inadequate, at least settled the principle of using the Observatory for medical research. Buzzard then persuaded Sir William Morris to provide £100,000 to be used to support Dr A. E. Barclay, a radiologist and personal friend of Morris who was interested in cineradiography. The Observatory was formally handed over to the University for medical school purposes in 1935 and Barclay remained in post until his death in 1948.

The idea of setting up a medical school at Oxford first occurred to Cairns in 1935 when he was returning from a trip to the USA; he was, at that time, head of the department of neurosurgery at the London Hospital. On his return from this trip, Cairns sent a three page letter to Farquhar Buzzard headed 'A proposal to establish a School of Medicine at Oxford', in which he suggested that this school of medicine should be small, consisting of not more than twenty students picked from the high fliers of the pre-clinical school in Oxford and also from other medical schools. They would receive three years of clinical training followed by six to eight years of training residencies.[14]

Farquhar Buzzard arranged a meeting between Cairns and Douglas Veale who was deeply impressed by Cairns' proposals. Cairns also enlisted the help of Sir Howard Florey with the idea of a medical school collaborating with the laboratories in South Parks Road.[15] The recruitment of Veale ensured that clinical medicine would, at last, be treated as a serious subject by the University. In 1936, Cairns produced a second memorandum, expanding the number of medical departments and stating clearly that the Nuffield Institute for Medical Research should become 'the pivot on which all other departments revolved'. The Observatory would become an institute for laboratory research because its architecture ruled out any prospect of turning it into hospital wards.[16]

What was needed, of course, was funds to put these ideas into practice. In July 1936, Farquhar Buzzard arranged a dinner party at All Souls College at which Lord Nuffield sat between Buzzard and the Vice-Chancellor, A. D. Lindsay, Master of Balliol. Halfway through the dinner Nuffield told Lindsay that he was prepared to donate two million pounds to the University for a medical school, adding that he had just had the greatest disappointment of his life by missing the opportunity to buy the Oxford Canal Company's basins and stores (an area now lying behind Nuffield College) where he had wanted to build 'the finest medical college in the world'. Quite how that would have fitted in with his plans for the Radcliffe Infirmary site is not clear but four days after the dinner

party Nuffield met Farquhar Buzzard and Cairns again and listened to Cairns' vision of the new medical school and where it should be.

Though still hankering after his plans for a medical college on the canal site, Nuffield was won round by Cairns' plans.[17] By the beginning of 1936, these four men – Lord Nuffield, Hugh Cairns, Farquhar Buzzard and Douglas Veale – not only saw eye-to-eye on the future of clinical medicine in Oxford but became close friends. They were the formidable driving force behind the transformation of clinical medicine in Oxford, and the sheer size of the donations by Nuffield, together with the appointment of very distinguished doctors to the Nuffield Professorships, ensured that clinical medicine would, indeed, be transformed.

A letter, dated 15 October 1936, was sent by Lord Nuffield to the Vice-Chancellor of the University of Oxford, announcing his plans and motives, which included the following passage:

> The basis of my proposal is that the University, offering as it does, an environment more favourable to research than in a big training Medical School, should widen the scope of its Medical School and of the Nuffield Institute for Medical Research ...

For this he proposed 'to give to the University in Trust sums which will amount, in the aggregate, to approximately one and a quarter million pounds'.[18]

In December 1936 a decree accepting Lord Nuffield's gift of £1,250,000 was approved by Congregation at a meeting in the Sheldonian Theatre. Nuffield was present when this was announced and he interrupted the proceedings by saying that he would increase his gift to the University to £2,000,000. Most interruptions of Congregation would be sternly condemned. This one, for obvious reasons, was not. It was gratefully accepted, and Nuffield was made an MA by decree.[19]

By the end of 1936 everything seemed to be in place for creating a new postgraduate medical school, in which the central feature – the word 'pivotal' was used more than once – would be the Nuffield Institute for Medical Research, housed in the Radcliffe Observatory. Nuffield Professors of Medicine, Surgery, Obstetrics and Gynaecology, and Anaesthetics would be appointed and would work at the Radcliffe Infirmary.[20] Gathorne Robert Girdlestone (1881-1950), an orthopaedic surgeon, had founded an orthopaedic hospital in 1922 in what used to be a convalescent home in Headington.[21] Nuffield, who had a special interest in helping crippled children, had already made a generous contribution to this hospital, after which it was named the Wingfield-Morris Hospital.[22] Girdlestone was appointed as the first Nuffield Professor of Orthopaedic Surgery in 1937.

As far as the Observatory was concerned, the two leading main subjects for medical research would be 'experimental therapeutics' and 'X-ray cinematography'. James Andrew Gunn (1882-1958) was appointed Nuffield Professor of Therapeutics and Director of the Nuffield Institute for Medical Research. Gunn was supposed to lead the research into experimental therapeutics while Dr Barclay, who offered to give his services free without salary and title, was in charge of research into X-ray cinematography.[23]

This, then, was the great vision for Oxford medicine: an elite medical school with special emphasis on research, and selected medical students who would, after qualification, be trained for several years in the techniques of medical research at a series of postgraduate clinical departments. At the centre of this vision would be the Nuffield Institute for Medical Research, supported not only by the clinical departments in the Radcliffe Infirmary and the Wingfield-Morris

Hospital, but working in close liaison with certain pre-clinical departments such as the Dunn School of Pathology. The Observatory, which could so easily have become no more than an empty architectural masterpiece, would now have a new and famous role. This was how it looked in the mid-1930s. It was nothing less than a highly ambitious plan to transform medicine in Oxford over the next ten years.

As soon as the University had accepted Lord Nuffield's donation, the management of the reformation of clinical medicine and research was placed in the hands of the Nuffield Committee for the Advancement of Medicine. Serendipity led to the appointment of Dr John Connybeare as an External Advisor. Connybeare had much to do with the advancement of medicine in London but had lived as a child in 13 Norham Gardens (which later became the home of William Osler, and most recently has become a property of the present owner of the Observatory, Green College). Within a matter of days after Nuffield's announcement of the gift of two million pounds, the first meeting of the Committee took place on the 12th December 1936. It is worth listing the members of this committee because it consisted of everyone who was instru-mental during the mid-1930s in reforming clinical medicine and establishing the Radcliffe Observatory as the home of the Nuffield Institute for Medical Research:

The Vice Chancellor of Oxford
    University
Professor Farquhar-Buzzard, Regius
    Professor of Medicine
[The Nuffield Professor of Clinical
    Medicine]
Hugh Cairns, Nuffield Professor of
    Surgery
[The Nuffield Professor of Obstetrics and
    Gynaecology]

Robert Macintosh, Nuffield Professor of
Anaesthetics

Gathorne Girdlestone (soon to be
appointed Nuffield Professor of
Orthopaedic Surgery)

Professor Gunn, Director of the Nuffield
Institute for Medical Research

Professor Florey, Professor of Pathology at
the Dunn School of Pathology

Professor Peters (Professor of
Biochemistry)

Dr Gibson, Mr Early and Mr Hyde from
the Radcliffe Infirmary

(The posts in this list enclosed in square
brackets are the Nuffield Professorships which
had not yet been filled. Those who were
appointed the following year were L. J. Witts,
Nuffield Professor of Medicine, and J. Chassar
Moir, Nuffield Professor of Obstetrics and
Gynaecology.)[24]

All the appointments had been made, and
the plans were beginning to fall into place,
when they were interrupted by the outbreak
of the Second World War. Fearing much
greater destruction of London by bombers
than actually occurred, the London teaching
hospitals evacuated most of their students to
provincial hospitals, including the Radcliffe
Infirmary which, in 1939, became a standard
type of medical school. The plans for a special,
elite, research-oriented medical school had to
be postponed for the duration.[25] When the
war ended, a meeting was held to decide
whether the original plans for an elite medical
school should be reintroduced, or whether it
should remain, as it had throughout the war,
as a standard medical school. There was a
heated debate, and the plan to revert to an elite
medical school with special emphasis on
research was lost by a very small margin.[26]

Part 2

The Observatory and The Nuffield Institute for Medical Research

Terence Ryan

This then is how and why the Radcliffe
Observatory came to be used for a
purpose for which it had never been
intended. Although it may have worked well
as a building from which to explore the
heavens, it was by no means ideal as an
institute for medical research. Indeed it might
be described as the oddest and most unsuitable
building ever used for an institute of medical
research. The rooms were excessively lofty,
with large ill-fitting windows designed to
accommodate telescopes, and the heating

system and water supply were archaic. There
was no lift and, because it was such a notable
historic building, permanent structural
alterations were not permissible. Nevertheless
the Nuffield Institute for Medical Research
occupied the Observatory for a total period
of some thirty-five years, from 1935-70.
For much of this time it was regarded by
many in Oxford as 'an ivory tower', isolated
not only from the medical school but,
geographically, from the other University
Science Departments in South Parks Road.

Many who remember looking into the building in the years immediately following the war remember it as a dusty and dingy place with an air of general neglect. Despite these drawbacks, the Institute gained a worldwide reputation for excellent innovating and basic work in several different fields, much of which was directly applicable to the practice of clinical medicine. Many of its occupants became heads of departments and made even greater discoveries in their later life.

The following account of how this was achieved is largely based on the personal recollections of those, still alive, who worked there in the postwar period. Additional sources of information are the obituary of Geoffrey Sharman Dawes (1918–96), the second and last Director of the Institute, written for the Royal Society by Sir Graham (Mont) Liggins,[27] and Geoffrey Dawes' own book on *Foetal and Neonatal Physiology*.[28]

The early years

The original aim of the Institute, to integrate medical research with the work of the Radcliffe Infirmary, was encapsulated in the two initial research subjects, experimental therapeutics and X-ray cinematography. In 1934 Professor Gunn (1882–1958), who had been Professor of Therapeutics in the University of Oxford since he was first recruited by Osler, was appointed Director of the Institute. At a meeting of the British Medical Association in Oxford in 1936 it was remarked that:

There has been no organized research in therapeutics in this country and no place where drugs used in medical practice can be subjected to independent searching tests by pharmacological as well as clinical methods. It is hoped that with the co-operation of the medical staff of the Infirmary the need may be met and new lines of therapeutic advance may be opened up.[29]

Although Professor Gunn was probably the source of this statement of intent, he did little research and contributed little to experimental therapeutics. His main concern was the editorship of the *British Pharmacopoeia*. In 1937 he occupied the Observer's House which was renamed Osler House at the request of Lord Nuffield. When later the medical students occupied the house at the instigation of Dr A. M. Cooke it became the centre for the Osler House Club. When it had been suggested that patients be bedded down in the Observatory it was Dr Cooke who took one look and vetoed the idea. In contrast, the Observatory was deemed suitable for animal research.

From the beginning significant advances were made in the use of X-ray cinematography. The protagonist of this technique was Alfred Barclay (1876–1948), affectionately known as 'Uncle B', who was already sixty when he was appointed to the staff of the Institute. He had had a distinguished career as a clinical radiologist in his native Manchester and in Cambridge where he had begun to develop equipment for cineradiography but had failed to persuade the University that radiology was a subject worthy of more support than the granting of a diploma. He was delighted to have the opportunity to continue this work on a full-time basis in Oxford.[30] Barclay was joined by K. J. Franklin, a physiologist who had already recognized the value of cineradiology as a non-invasive tool for the study of physiological phenomena. Together they used it to observe joint movements and the removal of dust from the airways by ciliary action. They are better known for their studies of foetal circulation, which were undertaken in collaboration with 'outsider', Sir Joseph Barcroft, Professor of Physiology in the University of Cambridge who was four years older than Barclay. Later dubbed 'The Father of Foetal Physiology' Barcroft had been interested in the subject since 1930 and, on hearing a paper given by

Franklin to the Physiological Society in 1936, he immediately sought the help of the Oxford team.

In 1946, Gunn resigned and Geoffrey Sharman Dawes CBE was appointed as Director of the Nuffield Institute of Medical Research. In his obituary of Dawes for the Royal Society in 1998, Sir Graham Liggins[31] describes the Institute as 'the best known and respected centre for research in foetal physiology'.[32] This was a remarkable achievement in view of the fact that the Observatory was far from ideal as the site for a research institute.

Early history: radiology

A remit attached to the first donation given by Morris for medical research directed that cineradiography should continue as one of the main subjects for research in the Institute, for it was seen as a tool likely to attract cooperation between clinicians and scientists. It was thought that the combination of X-ray cinematography and therapeutics would throw light not only on clinical but on anatomical, physiological and pharmaco-logical problems.[33]

Cineradiography was a means of recording for the first time *in vivo* studies of actual blood flow and circulation. Hugh Cairns, the Nuffield Professor of Surgery, took a great interest in cineradiography as a way of exploring the blood supply to the brain. It was also used to visualize and analyze moving physiological functions such as the emptying of the bladder, the peristaltic movements of the gut, and phenomena such as swallowing. The need for understanding these activities was driven by physiologists. K. J. Franklin was the first of these to take an interest in the potentials of cineradiography, and applied it to a recently delivered lamb lying by its mother still attached to the placenta.

The radiologist who developed the technique was A. E. Barclay and the funds were donated by Lord Nuffield. Barclay wrote

several books[34] and there is a Barclay medal awarded by the British Institute of Radiology. In 1939 Dr F. H. Kemp was appointed as the first full-time radiologist at the Radcliffe Infirmary; he participated in discussions about research in the Institute but he had no formal position. Dr J. P. Curtis, who developed cerebral angiography with Sir Hugh Cairns also collaborated with the Institute.

The Second World War had a tremendous influence on all aspects of medicine, and this included the Nuffield Institute for Medical Research. Some of the most significant work undertaken there was related to the prevalent problems of war injury, and it is not surprising that one of the leaders in the management of the injured – later to become Nuffield Professor of Orthopaedics – was Joseph Trueta. Following his experience of treating war injury during the Spanish Civil War, he wrote a well-known book on war surgery, with special reference to the biological method of treatment of wounds and fractures.[35]

He wrote in 1946:

In March, 1941, while Britain was suffering heavily from air raids, Bywaters and Beall published the first contemporary account of a post-traumatic condition which they had recognized and for which they coined the name 'crush syndrome'; they reported four cases in which the victims had died from kidney failure after having had one or more limbs crushed for several hours under fallen masonry stones or heavy beams. In these four cases, as in others subsequently reported, there were several features in common, including: 1. A continuous compression of one or more limbs (usually, though not invariably, the legs). 2. In most instances, temporary improvement of the patient after release from the compression. 3. Progressive impairment of kidney function until death from renal failure occurred about a week after the infliction of the injury. The clinical picture of the syndrome became steadily clearer as more cases were recognized and reported. In some of the cases published, there was not only evidence of impairment of renal function, but there were also indications of impairment of the circulation in the injured limb, such as coldness and the development of oedema and blisters, but at necropsy these cases showed neither evidence of gross damage to the main arteries nor the presence of emboli or thrombi in these vessels.

It was Joseph Trueta who had considered that this syndrome was not due to toxic substances liberated by the crushed tissues, but due to spasm of the main arteries of the affected limb, spreading up to involve the renal arteries. He was able to do so because:

> It has been of great good fortune to me that the Nuffield Institute for Medical Research, Oxford, holds the door open to clinicians with problems to solve. The idea of this research centre, in which radiological techniques are employed as the basis of experimental studies, was due entirely to the vision of the physiologist of our team (K. J. Franklin), who brought to his aid a radiologist of long-standing experience (A. E. Barclay); the latter in his turn introduced the third collaborator of the Nuffield Institute research team who was Marjorie M. L. Prichard.[36]

Trueta later described how, because of the war, it was impossible to undertake more than a preliminary investigation, and that it was not until the war was over that they were able to take up the research fully. They took only three months of research to clinch the study which showed that the blood supply of the kidney was shut down when the limbs were crushed.

Immediately after the war, Gordon Ardran was appointed as the radiologist to take the cineradiology forward. Graham Liggins describes Ardran thus:

> Ardran became one of Britain's most distinguished radiologists, publishing prolifically, and was recognized as a pioneer in the field. His work at the Institute in the west wing of the Observatory moved towards clinical applications, including swallowing, speech and bladder function, for which cine-radiographic techniques were essential.[37]

The Observatory became home for many important advances. Some activities are worth recording here because the image they describe shows more about human behaviour than is revealed in an X-ray film. There are many who remember these cineradiology studies, and many medical students of that time were used as experimental subjects. These studies were the foundation stones of a now well-recognized discipline of respiratory physiology and of the management of sleep apnoea.

William Lund, Consultant Ear, Nose and Throat Surgeon to the Radcliffe Infirmary, who was researching the physiological process of swallowing in 1963-4, describes how an experimental subject was encouraged to drink eight pints of beer at the Royal Oak (a public house opposite the Radcliffe Infirmary) and was then brought back to drink a ninth pint of beer mixed with a radio-opaque material, and hung upside-down by his ankles to demonstrate the effectiveness of swallowing and the prevention of reflux.

Mr Lund was also involved in the study of sword-swallowing. Not only did cineradiography reveal how the process was done, but it was a means of getting to know the eccentric practitioners of this profession. Gordon Ardran had for a long time wanted to make a film of someone performing this manoeuvre, and eventually discovered a gentleman who practised 'the art' at the St Giles Fair. He persuaded him to attend the Institute, everything was set up and the loop of film was duly made, only to find it was quite useless. The X-ray camera had been aimed from the side, and as soon as the performer lifted up his hands to place the sword vertically above his mouth, the shoulders and upper arms got in the way.

Because a lateral film rather than a front view was desirable in order to show the passage of the sword through the pharynx, down the oesophagus and into the stomach, the experts had to work out a solution to this radiographic problem. It was finally solved by an unsuspecting secretary being summoned from an adjoining office who then stood on a pile of books behind the subject and, with fear and trembling, inserted the sword into his mouth. Meanwhile, the sword-swallower was standing 'rigid to attention', arms by his side, and his head thrown back with perspiration breaking out on his forehead. The secretary then gradually pushed the sword down, with the wretched performer giving frantic signals with his head and hands to alter the direction of the sword. The whole procedure was, of course, analogous to the passing of a rigid endoscope. It was completed without any complications and the cine film successfully accomplished.

Gordon Ardran might reasonably have expected to succeed Professor Gunn as Director of the Nuffield Institute for Medical Research but it was Geoffrey Dawes who was appointed.

Dawes had practised as a General Practitioner during the latter part of the war because his asthma made him unfit for military service. He undertook his research degree in the Pharmacology Department under J. H. Burn, Professor of Pharmacology, where most of the work was more akin to physiology. The offer of the Directorship of the Institute came out of the blue because he had not applied for the job and Professor Burn had already obtained funding for him to work in the USA. Dawes confided in David Whitteridge that he had no idea how he would sustain a research programme but he was assured that one thing would lead to another and he would either sink or swim.

However, his relationship with Ardran

was not easy. Dawes repeatedly let it be known that cineradiographic techniques were, in his opinion, not worthwhile and he was not always tactful when he did so. A colleague vividly recalls an occasion when all the members of the Institute, including technicians and secretaries, were gathered around the afternoon tea table (as was the rule) when he suddenly made an ironic joke 'I think radiology is a very useful subject.' There was dead silence because everyone knew his views on radiology. Then he added slowly and deliberately: 'Yes, I really do: it provides film boxes, which are very useful for storing kymograph records.' (Much of the early equipment of this period in the Observatory was makeshift. To project the cine-films, Gordon Ardran had purchased a projector from one of the local cinemas for five pounds. Loops of film were hung from the top of the staircase, as were the long sheets of kymographs from the physiological studies.)

Dawes resented the clause in the Institute's statutes which required its use for radiology. What other laboratory, he argued, is restricted to the use of a specific technique? That, of course, was to ignore the fact that one of the main reasons for founding the Institute was research into radiology. Indeed, some might have argued (and Ardran probably did) that Dawes was failing in his duties as Director by not pursuing the objectives for which the Institute was founded. However, the 'radiological clause' which linked the programme to a single technique was eventually removed from the statute – the Institute for Medical Research clearly, by virtue of its name, having a wider remit.

Neonatal physiology 1946-70

It was the study of so many aspects of neonatal physiology that brought to Oxford a large number of research workers to work with Geoffrey Dawes. Some of these researchers were distinguished clinicians from the USA and elsewhere. Others were young clinicians wanting to be trained in research methods and some of them became significant leaders of the medical research establishment in various parts of the world; there is no doubt that the Nuffield Institute had a worldwide reputation.

As we have seen, it was inappropriate to use an eighteenth century monumental Observatory as an animal laboratory for research. Sheep were the principal experimental subjects but there was nowhere to house the sheep. They had to be herded or carried up the stone staircase. There were various descriptions of how the sheep were encouraged to arrive on the first floor of the Observatory. One trick was to have a plank at their side, pushing them against the wall. Apparently the sheep imagined that this was the same sensation as moving with a flock of sheep, and they were happy to pursue the directive forces of the plank as it was moved by the attendant up the staircase. Others described how four assistants would lift the sheep on to a mat which was hauled up to the first floor.

Gordon Ardran's radiology department was on the ground floor in the west wing of the Observatory while Dawes' office was in east wing.[38] The east wing, comprising the director's office also contained the supporting physics/mechanical workshop and electronics workshop activities, and the small X-ray room which had in it a fine focus low-voltage X-ray set. This room was mainly used by Dr Maureen Owen for bone studies under the supervision of Dame Janet Vaughan, a world leader in the field of radioactive isotopes. When Janet Vaughan moved to the Churchill Hospital, Gordon Ardran used her room to house a small cayman in a domestic bath. The cayman was a subject for a large range of studies on the mechanism of swallowing. Not surprisingly this gave rise to the apocryphal story that this was simply a ploy by Ardran to maintain occupancy of the room! Later the room became an office and was occupied for a short period by Dr M. K. Bevir, who had

recently completed his Cambridge PhD on a most elegant three-dimensional mathematical analysis of electromagnetic flowmeters.

The rooms in the main building were used as follows. The main entrance was used mainly at tea and coffee time, and was where much of the work and the development of ideas took place. At Christmas it was used for a staff party with a bust of Lord Nuffield dressed appropriately as Santa Claus. The doors from the entrance hall to the garden normally remained closed and were seldom used except by those who took their sandwich lunch into the garden. The centre piece of the grand entrance hall was the eighteenth century pedestal table which later was moved to the top floor of the Tower of the Winds with the original library steps. By the year 2000 this table was deteriorating as a result of too much sun exposure. Nonetheless, valued at £90,000, it exited ignobly through a window of the Tower of the Winds lifted by a very large crane on its way to the auction house. The proceeds from its sale were used in part to commission the current oak furniture in the dining room.

Space was always a problem in the building and storage included such places as trap-doors in the floor of the main room on the first floor. The adjoining room to the west was previously used as the darkroom. The top floor was always used as the library. It was, and still is, too hot in the summer and too cold in the winter, and the flies which lived in the walls and ceiling and in the top floor plaster work would come out on the first hot day and in the autumn they would die in their thousands.

On the 10th March 1971 the Postgraduate Medical Library of the Radcliffe Infirmary was destroyed by fire. The Deputy Librarian, Maureen Forrest, had recently been appointed to develop co-operation between libraries and found herself in receipt of a consignment of a quarter of a ton of bound journals from the British Medical Association.

These were stored at the top of the Tower of the Winds and Radcliffe Infirmary porters were not pleased to be given the job of carrying them up the spiral staircase. Maureen Forrest recalls making large numbers of meringues as a bribe and token of thanks. She also recalls that the volumes were stored for two years, by which time they were thickly covered in dead flies and, it being a warm August, there was an exceptional and revolting number of dying flies to be disposed of before the volumes were carried downstairs again.

In an adjoining room to the east of the laboratory on the first floor a mezzanine floor was inserted, constructed on scaffolding, and accessed by a steep ladder. It was used for analysis of samples derived from experiments on the sheep on the lower floor. The lofty rooms meant that several of the laboratories had similar mezzanine structures. Water supply was always a problem since most of it came from a tank at the top of the tower. This did not generate sufficient pressure to operate the filter pumps needed for biochemical work, all of which had to be done in the Animal House built to the West of the Observatory.

The Animal House, on the site now occupied by the Green College residential block known as the Doll Building, had no mains water and yet all of the biochemical work was done at this site. The building continued to be used by the Nuffield Institute even when most of the team had moved up to the Headington site because it had very good facilities for small animal work including an operating theatre which could be used for sterile surgery. Graham Liggins worked there for just under six months, solely on chronic sheep preparations, where the foetus had been operated on and returned to the uterus, although the facilities for this sort of work were woefully inadequate. In the Animal House there were rooms for rats, rabbits and guinea pigs – and for a short time, a coypu who escaped and destroyed some of the electric wiring. There was a yard at the back of the building where sheep could be held for short periods, where a pair of goats stripped all the green paint from the doors.

One of the drawbacks was that it was necessary to walk backwards and forwards in all weathers and frequently at night between the Animal House and the main building, carrying samples for analysis from the sheep room to Heather Shelley's room.

In addition to the main building, there were two small circular buildings originally for housing telescopes (Plate 52, p. 101). These were known as the two 'rotundas'. The Eastern Rotunda was a centre for glassblowing for several hospital departments, and was to continue to do so under the supervision of Phil Tosh, one-time chauffeur to the Nuffield Professor of Anaesthetics, Sir Robert Macintosh, well into the early years of Green College. The Western Rotunda housed Medical Artists, Audrey Arnott and Fay McLarty and their prize-winning dachshunds, all from Hugh Cairns' Department in London. Both artists were described as extroverted, sparkling and suitably unconventional. They were the founders of The Medical Artists Association of Great Britain. For a short period the Western Rotunda was used as a records department and as bedrooms for a few doctors.

G. J. Fraenkel, in his biography of Sir Hugh Cairns, reported a controversy concerning ownership of this building: 'since the original boundary line, it was said, had been drawn up somewhat light-heartedly after an ample lunch'.[39] The workshop was established there by the Department of Surgery and the Department of Haematology, and its first technician was a Mr A. Lord, 'one of a family of Oxford technicians'. One of the technicians in the Rotunda was Heinz Woolf, who later took a BSc in Physiology at University College, London and took up a post at the National Institute of Medical Research at Mill Hill. He later became Director of the Brunel Institute of

Bioengineering at Brunel University. He published prolifically and presented popular television science programmes.

Technical expertise

Besides cineradiography, other techniques were developed. The Institute needed a Physicist and in 1949 Derek Wyatt was appointed. He had been working in the Clarendon Laboratory for a D.Phil. on the production and measurement of high energy radiation and completed his studies at Worcester College. Graham Liggins wrote of Wyatt's reactions:

> Wyatt recalls his arrival as an enormous culture shock. He had come from one of the premier physics laboratories in the country where he had been working on an electron accelerator at the cutting edge of scientific technology. Dawes had been in the Institute for only a year, but to his credit had mastered the elements of valve amplifiers, among other things. He had engaged an electronics technician to make these and a welder to make the supporting frames. But the high-grade workshop and electronic services, which for three years Wyatt had taken for granted, were entirely absent. He, on the other hand, had no professional knowledge of any biological subject. Over the next few years, Dawes and Wyatt learned to look at things from new viewpoints and rapidly built up the facilities. Wyatt recalls it as a dramatic, very hard-working and exciting period when all the staff moulded themselves into an effective interdisciplinary force. It was made clear to the technicians that they were at the cutting edge and nothing but the best would do. They were always given the opportunity of seeing the instruments they had made at work. Dawes was usually charming, good-humoured and popular with the technicians, but there were lapses. On one occasion, the chief technician threatened to bring all the technicians out on strike.[40]

Derek Wyatt had responsibility for overseeing the development of the Workshops and remembers laying the gas pipes with Bill Dodson who was an ex-shipyard worker and who later became a pillar of great strength in the workshop. Wyatt wrote:

> … in connection with the unsuitability of the Observatory as a laboratory for medical research, of the fact that the main rooms on the ground floor are 'corridor' rooms. This was particularly inconvenient for me, as my lab was sandwiched between the Director's room and the workshops. Much of my development work required extremely sensitive instrumentation. This could dart off-scale and take some time to recover, when the splendid teak floorboards moved with the pressure of the Director's steps as he visited the workshops; or similarly when the technicians visited the lavatories, which were off the main entrance hall. I would then wait in trepidation for the Return Journey. This resulted in a good deal of night work by me. To offset some of these difficulties, when a heavy second hand milling machine was acquired, it was mounted on a stone foundation discovered beneath the floor boards which was originally the foundation for the telescope.[41]

John Vane, who later became a Nobel Prize winner, recalls that it was a great period of his life, for the Institute bustled with life, and there were students and post-doctoral students from all over the world. He and his family were rather impecunious, living first in a caravan and then moving around friends' houses (including the Dawes's home) while they were on holiday. The Home Office required that animals should be incinerated at the end of experiments, but they did not stipulate the degree of incineration. One of John Vane's roles while meat rationing was in force was disposal of the sheep, and the preparation of cuts of meat for cooking by the staff of the Institute. This was of course a period of rationing, which continued well after the War.

Apparently the anaesthetic agent nembutal is destroyed by cooking so no one was affected by somnolence.

At the time of the Nuffield Institute for Medical Research, anemometers were still kept on the roof. There was an exit through a wooden door and a rather rickety wooden staircase up to the roof of the Observatory, where one could walk around in a drainage gully that had no railings. The anemometers were read daily. Derek Wyatt reports that the anemometer shafts passed through the roof terminating in revolution counters which were situated on the wall on the left of the staircase. A technician from the School of Geography, Timothy Birt, came each day to make his measurements and was known as 'The Ghost', because he never spoke a word. The Observatory experienced some of the most extreme weather at that time, as there were several very cold winters especially in 1957 and 1963. One of the users of the Observatory spent days in his naval greatcoat.

A key member of the research staff, Heather Shelley, had a room overlooking the gardens to the south. The gardens were the play area for the medical students of Osler House. The entrance from the Observatory into the garden was closed most of the time. Not until the advent of Green College did the Observatory turn its face to the north and open its doors to what was to become the College garden so well described in Chapter 3.

Although conditions were difficult, with inadequate laboratory materials, Geoffrey Dawes followed the tradition described by Trueta and saw to it that clinicians had the opportunity to receive a superb training in research methods and in evaluation of the results. Visitors came from various parts of the world, including Eastern Europe. They included Julius Mestyan, Professor of Paediatrics in the University of Pecs, who was described as an exotic physiologist from Hungary who was used to double glazed windows and complained of a cold English bedroom in North Oxford. While working on heat control in new born animals he would keep warm by working late at the Institute.

During the final years of the occupation of the Observatory by the Nuffield Institute for Medical Research plans were developed to move the Institute to the Headington site and the Tower of the Winds was designated as a suitable site for the Medical School Library but this plan was later abandoned. In 1970, the Nuffield Institute for Medical Research moved to the Headington site.

1971 to the advent of Green College

In 1971, the Department of Clinical Biochemistry in the Radcliffe Infirmary was in urgent need of expansion, and took over the east wing of the Observatory where Peter Esnouf continued his studies of blood coagulation factors. The room immediately to the right of the main entrance became a seminar room. On the first floor, the Gibson Room was taken over by the Director of Postgraduate Studies. The current dining room was at first used by Martin Vessey for his study of the contraceptive pill, and later by Gerald Draper with the Oxford Childhood Cancer Study. Also on this floor, the Fellows' Room, which had been divided in two by inserting a mezzanine floor, was used by others working in the field of epidemiology such as Leo Kinlen's research assistants who worked in the lower half and Nick Wald's research assistants above. The Tower of the Winds was used by an inveterate smoking statistician and an artist, who were banished there from a lower floor. From time to time various excrescences appeared on the building. There was a very ugly hut on the roof for meteorological measurements and when the roof was re-leaded in 1978 large huts shielded the workmen.

This essay describes the Observatory's strange occupancy by the Nuffield Institute for Medical Research during three decades.

Some of the achievements of science were to have profound clinical benefits. As a listener to the 'goings on' in the Observatory, the author has been impressed by the fact that many of the world's greatest twentieth century scientists have walked through its doors and acquired skills used for later achievements. At the same time, the building has imposed upon its occupiers some eccentricities and the anecdotes reported here give life to a period which for most of the present occupants has been an unopened book.

As a physician, John Radcliffe would have been pleased that the Radcliffe Trustees ensured that his money has been well spent to the benefit of medicine, and the unusual use of the Observatory was in this sense appropriate.

NOTES

1. This is a simplified account of the arrangements which were made in the 1770s, and of the people involved. For a full account see Guest, I. (1991) *John Radcliffe and his Trust.* The Radcliffe Trust, London. 230-2
2. In Oxford, when students complete their pre-clinical stage, they graduate with the degree of BA in the school of physiological sciences.
3. A large majority went to one of the London teaching hospitals, but a few went to teaching hospitals in other cities.
4. Fraenkel, G.J. (1991) *Hugh Cairns. First Nuffield Professor of Surgery, University of Oxford.* Oxford University Press, Oxford. 118
5. British Medical Association (1936) *The Book of Oxford.* Printed for the 104th annual meeting of the British Medical Association, London.
6. Bearn, A. (1993) *Archibald Garrod and the Individuality of Man.* Clarendon Press, Oxford; Lock, S., Last, J. M. and Dunea, G. (2001) *The Oxford Illustrated Companion to Medicine.* Oxford University Press, Oxford. 337.
7. Bearn (1993) 18-121.
8. Bearn (1993) 115-16.
9. Fraenkel (1991) 103.
10. Cooke, A. M. (1994) *My first Seventy-Five Years of Medicine.* Royal College of Physicians of London. 39.

11. The importance of Douglas Veale's involvement at the earliest stages of planning a new medical school was that he wielded great power within the University and was instrumental in bringing to an end the University's indifference towards clinical medicine.
12. William Richard Morris, Viscount Nuffield (1877-1963). Lord Nuffield was the oldest of a family of seven of whom only a sister survived beyond an early age. He grew up in Cowley where he went to the village school, and at the age of 24 was a maker of cycles. By 1910 he advertised himself as a motor car agent and produced the Morris Oxford in 1912. Working at first in Longwall, Oxford, he soon moved to Temple Cowley and the firm of Morris Motors was incorporated in 1919. The Morris Cowley followed, and after weathering the slump of 1920-1, he was, by 1926, producing a third of the national output of cars. In 1931 he produced the popular Morris Minor. Soon he had made a fortune of £20 million. In 1929 Morris was created a baronet, in 1934 a baron as Lord Nuffield and in 1938 a viscount. Nuffield had already made contributions to medicine outside Oxford before we come to the events described in this chapter.
13. Guest (1991) 114 –15 and 221-2.
14. Fraenkel (1991) 101-2.
15. Howard Florey (later Sir Howard Florey) was Professor of Pathology at the Dunn School of Pathology in South Parks Road and was the leader of the team which produced penicillin.
16. Fraenkel (1991) 109. In the 1930s, Dr A. M. Cooke inspected the Observatory to see if could be adapted to contain a hospital ward or wards. It was obvious at once that this was not a possibility.
17. Fraenkel (1991) 110-12.
18. University Archives, Bodleian Library. *Proceedings of the Nuffield Committee for the Advancement of Medicine.* FA/6/5/2.
19. Fraenkel (1991)117; University Archives, Bodleian Library, *Proceedings of the Nuffield Committee for the Advancement of Medicine,* FA/6/5/2.
20. The appointment of (Sir) Robert Macintosh as Nuffield Professor of Anaesthetics was

controversial. No one in medicine at the time considered anaesthetics an academic subject worthy of such a post. However, Lord Nuffield happened, some years earlier, to have been given an anaesthetic by Mackintosh in London for dental treatment and was so impressed by the painlessness of the procedure (unlike previous unhappy experiences) that he absolutely insisted against the advice of everyone else that there must be a Nuffield Chair in Anaesthetics and that the first holder must be Robert Mackintosh. Only when he threatened to withdraw his donation to all Nuffield posts did medical resistance crumble. Lord Nuffield was, of course, right. The work done by the Nuffield Department of Anaesthetics was magnificent.

21. Duthie, R. (1987) *Fifty Years of the Nuffield Professorship of Orthopaedic Surgery in the University of Oxford 1937-87*. Privately printed. 2.
22. It is now called the Nuffield Orthopaedic Centre.
23. University Archives, Bodleian Library. *Proceedings of the Nuffield Committee for the Advancement of Medicine*. FA/6/5/1.
24. University Archives, Bodleian Library. FA/6/5/1-5.
25. The conversion of the Radcliffe Infirmary to a wartime teaching hospital was undertaken at ten days' notice by Dr A. M. Cooke, Honorary Physician to the Radcliffe Infirmary. Personal communication.
26. Cooke, A. M. (1991) *The Cooke's Tale*. Holywell Press, Oxford.
27. Liggins, G. (1998) Geoffrey Sharman Dawes (1918-1996). *Biographical Memoirs of the Royal Society*. 44: 109-25.
28. Dawes, G. (1968) *Foetal and Neonatal Physiology*. Year Book Medical Publishers Inc, Chicago.
29. British Medical Association (1936).
30. Golding S. J. *A. E. Barclay and angiographic research in Oxford in the nineteen-forties*.
31. Sir Graham Liggins, CBE FRS, of the Department of Obstetrics and Gynaecology, Auckland School of Medicine and Health Sciences, University of Auckland, New Zealand,
32. Liggins, G. (1998).
33. British Medical Association (1936).
34. Barclay, A. E. (1943) *Radiology: Empiricism or Science?* Oxford; Barclay, A. E. (1944) *K. J. Franklin: The Foetal Circulation and Cardiovascular System*. Blackwell's Scientific Publications, Oxford.
35. Trueta, J. (1946) *The Principles and Practices of War Surgery*. Hamish Hamilton, London.
36. Trueta, J., Barclay, A. E., Franklin, K. J., Daniel, P. M. and Prichard, M. M. L. (1947) *Studies of the Renal Circulation*. Blackwell Scientific Publications, Oxford.
37. Liggins, G. (1998).
38. Derek Wyatt (Personal communication to Terence Ryan).
39. Fraenkel, G. J. (1991).

Chapter 7

Green College at the Radcliffe Observatory

Jeffery Burley and Irvine Loudon

Over a period of 225 years three major sets of activities within the Radcliffe Observatory brought with them significant changes in the structure and use of the building. The quiet, persistent and scholarly research of Georgian and Victorian astronomers and climatic observers was replaced by the sometimes frenetic research of a range of groups of medical scientists within the Nuffield Institute of Medical Research; they sought urgent answers to problems of immediate concern to human health but were often supported for only short terms and with limited finance.

When the astronomers had left, for a short time the Observatory was used as the Department of the Regius Professor of Medicine, and there was also an office for the Director of the Postgraduate Study of Medical Education (John Potter). To understand the full impact it is desirable to consider something of the background to the University's thinking about colleges in general and graduate colleges in particular during the latter third of the twentieth century.

The Oxford college system

A stranger who came to Oxford to study the traditional colleges in the centre of the city would soon recognize the features they had in common. The oldest colleges were modelled on medieval houses and were, in effect, boarding houses where young scholars twelve to sixteen years old could live under some kind of authority and discipline. In spite of wide differences in architectural periods and styles, most colleges were constructed on a plan of quadrangles, often with cloisters, from which staircases led to rooms for undergraduates and Fellows. Other features included common rooms (senior and junior), dining hall, library, chapel, lawns, gardens and, just inside the entrance to the college, a lodge staffed by college porters.

Visitors to Oxford are often surprised that all the traditional colleges have undergraduates and Fellows working in a wide variety of disciplines. None is devoted to a single subject; there is no college of modern languages, law, or philosophy, for example. In the earliest days of the University the young scholars were taught in the centralized University 'Schools'; lecture theatres in the traditional colleges were conspicuous by their absence or small size. Sciences are almost totally taught within the University departments, such as the Departments of Chemistry, Geography and Zoology. Teaching is still largely based on the tutorial system; this was introduced some time after the first colleges were founded, and in tutorials small numbers of students (one to four) were typically taught in Fellows' college rooms (occasionally supplemented if the students were lucky by a glass of sherry). In the sciences, although some tutorials are still conducted in scientists' college rooms, most take place in the University's science departments, often in groups of ten or twelve, and most courses have a heavy load of lectures and practical laboratory or field exercises (while the provision of sherry is rare for reasons of laboratory safety as much as the lecturer's poverty).

This is the 'Oxbridge system' with which all present or past members of the Universities of Oxford and Cambridge are familiar. However, these traditional undergraduate colleges have been supplemented by a series of graduate colleges, all of which apart from All Souls (founded in 1438) and Nuffield College (founded in 1937), have been founded since the second world war: St Antony's in 1948, Wolfson College (initially known as Iffley College), St Cross College, and Linacre College in 1965, Green College in 1979 and Kellogg College in 1994. Although the graduate colleges contain many of the features seen in the traditional colleges, some have chosen to foster some degree of specialization - Nuffield College, for example, has concentrated on the social sciences, St Antony's College on foreign affairs, and Green College on clinical medicine and the medical sciences.

The special features and medical origins of Green College

Green College is not only one of the youngest graduate colleges to be established in Oxford, but it is the one in which there is a greater representation of clinical medicine than in any other college. (Nevertheless, in spite of some beliefs to the contrary, it is now, as we will see, far from being a purely medical college.) It is also the only college in the University in which the central physical feature is a magnificent eighteenth-century building that

was originally designed for another purpose. This is the subject of this book, the Radcliffe Observatory, which has been described by some as the finest eighteenth-century building in Oxford, and by Nicholas Pevsner as 'the architecturally finest observatory in Europe'.

Although the concept of a home for post-graduate medicine in Oxford had been debated through much of the twentieth century, the College may be considered to be the brain-child and product of Sir Richard Doll, the Founder Warden (Plate 54, p. 156); he is recognized as one of the world's leading epidemiologists and is famous for establishing the link between smoking tobacco and human lung cancer. He was Regius Professor of Medicine in Oxford University from 1969 until 1979 when he took up the post of Warden of Green College having been instrumental in securing the conceptual agreement of the University and the financial support of Dr Cecil Green, the Founder Benefactor (Plate 55, p. 156).

The original intention was that Green College should indeed be essentially a college for medical tutors, scientists and students, largely because at that time the old colleges were not interested in clinical medicine with the result that there were many clinical teachers entitled to a college Fellowship but unable to obtain one. There were also NHS teachers who were left in the cold and had no access to any of the colleges until they were made Common Room members of Green College. None of the old colleges took any interest in the welfare of the clinical students, let alone provide accommodation for them, until Green College was established; then the old colleges suddenly became aware of the needs of clinical students and began to offer them accommodation.

During the 1970s, plans for what was intended to become known as Radcliffe College, passed through various University committees, and in autumn 1975 the

'Committee on a Proposed Medical Graduate Society' stated that the aim of such a society should be to 'meet the academic and social needs of senior and junior members of the medical school'. The crucial decision was made by the Conference of Colleges in 1976, when a solid majority of the Conference voted in favour. The Hebdomadal Council promulgated a Statute in January 1977 authorizing the foundation of Radcliffe College at some future date. At the same time, it published a decree allocating the Observatory and its associated buildings and grounds for the use of the College.

From the beginning, therefore, it was decided that the college should be centred on the Radcliffe Observatory, and that membership of the new college would be largely, but not completely, confined to clinical medicine. The 'society' should consist of clinical students and about 35 Fellows. A large majority of Fellows would be medical, but a few would be senior academics and administrative members of the University not from the Faculty of Clinical Medicine. These would form the Governing Body of the College, and the first meeting of the Governing Body Elect took place in the Board Room of the Radcliffe Infirmary on the 8th December 1977, following at least two meetings of the Radcliffe College Consultative Committee. Two years later, in 1979, when initial appointments had been made, the minutes of the Governing Body showed that it consisted of thirty Fellows.

Funding, naming and establishing the College

For the College to become a reality, the Observatory had to be refurbished, and new buildings erected. Funding was obviously a major difficulty. Sir Richard Doll raised £250,000 from various sources, including the Radcliffe Trust, the E. P. Abraham Educational Trust, the Rhodes Trust, Blackwell Scientific Publications, and the pharmaceutical firm

Searle. In the autumn of 1976, Professor Beeson suggested that Dr Cecil Green of Texas Instruments might be persuaded to provide financial support. Dr William Gibson, Professor of Medical History at the University of British Columbia, who knew Dr Green well, offered to contact him. A letter, together with the gift of an Ackerman print of the Observatory, was duly delivered to Dr Green.

Dr Cecil Green was born near Manchester, emigrated to the USA when he was two years old, and was in San Francisco during the earthquake of 1906. His undergraduate education was at the University of British Columbia and he moved on to graduate study in electrical engineering at the Massachusetts Institute of Technology. He worked at first for a small oil exploration company which he and four colleagues subsequently bought from its owner just before the Japanese bombed Pearl Harbour. It looked as if they were faced by ruin until they discovered that one of their instruments could detect submarines; the instrument division consequently expanded to become Texas Instruments, with Dr Green in charge.

When Dr Cecil Green and his wife Ida (Plate 55, p. 156) first visited Oxford in April 1977 they stayed for only four days, but he signed a contract before he left for home in which he agreed to provide funds. Initially he provided £1 million, in stages, and on condition that the first part of the construction contract was let by the end of December 1977. The Director of the Ashmolean Museum brought a committee of the Fine Art Commission to look at the plans. This committee gave warm approval to the idea of converting the Observatory into a college and this proved crucial in obtaining planning approval from Oxford City Council.

Later, Dr Green provided another £1,375,000, including £730,000 for the Walton Building and part of the McAlpine Quadrangle. There is no doubt at all that, without funding on this scale, the College would not have been established.

The College thus became Green College, a title confirmed by University Statute in November 1977. Sir Richard Doll, who had skilfully steered the entire project from the very beginning, was the 'Warden Elect' and was formally appointed as the first Warden on 1 September 1977; he was ably supported by his Vice-Warden (initially termed Vice-Gerent), Dr Brian Bower, a National Health Service Consultant Paediatrician. It is no secret that the Radcliffe Trust was upset by the change of name (the possibility of calling it Radcliffe-Green College was dismissed) but the Trust was partly pacified by the assurance that the College address would always be 'Green College, at the Radcliffe Observatory, Woodstock Road, Oxford'. The College was officially opened on 13 June 1981, by the then University Chancellor, Sir Harold Macmillan.

The diversification of Green College

The almost exclusive focus on a single set of academic disciplines in the medical sector was not typical of the composition of Oxford and Cambridge colleges where, in undergraduate colleges particularly, multi-disciplinarity was the rule; by this it was felt that academic staff interactions would be fostered and students more widely educated. Subsequently the Governing Body, under Sir Richard's leadership, began to broaden the subject coverage of both its Fellows and students. In addition it agreed to create a group of associated members of the Common Room who were academically equivalent to the University's professors and lecturers but were working as National Health Service Consultants or on research programmes in University departments, typically financed by external sources and with no formal assignment by the University to a college.

The second and third Wardens were Sir John (later Lord) Walton, a neurologist who was formerly Dean of Medicine at Newcastle University and President of the General Medical Council (Plate 56, p. 157) and Sir Crispin Tickell, formerly British Ambassador to Mexico, Permanent Secretary of the Overseas Development Administration, and British Permanent Representative to the United Nations (Plate 58, p. 157); their tenures were separated by a year during which the then Vice-Warden, Dr Trevor Hughes, a neuropathologist in the Radcliffe Infirmary, was Acting Warden (Plate 57, p. 157). During Sir Crispin's tenure the Governing Body approved the establishment of an Advisory Council with HRH Princess Anne as one of the first members (Plates 60 and 61, p. 158); the Council meets annually to advise the Warden and the Governing Body on emerging issues and future developments.

The next two Vice-Wardens were Mr Julian Britton, a general surgeon, and Professor Terence Ryan, NHS Consultant and later the University's Professor of Dermatology. They all continued the process of expansion and diversification of the college's Fellowship and student body. Julian Britton maintained a smooth transition of the Wardenship from Sir John Walton to Sir Crispin Tickell. Terence Ryan provided the support necessary for Sir Crispin to maintain his demanding schedule of international and national policy advice, speaking engagements and media interviews that gave Green College considerable public attention. Terence Ryan also had a strong commitment to maintaining the College-NHS Consultant link and brought with him to the post a long history of association with the Osler Society, the Medical Student Society (Osler House Club) and the development of links with alumni.

Sir Crispin established Working Parties chaired by Professor Ryan's successor as Vice-Warden, Professor Jeffery Burley, Director of the Oxford Forestry Institute, to prepare formal strategic plans for the College in the 1990s and into the new millennium. These gave rise *inter alia* to the current mission statement of Green College:

> The mission of Green College is to provide academic, administrative and social support for Fellows, Students, Common Room Members and Academic Visitors working in pure and applied subjects related to human health and welfare.

This shows that the college maintains human health as its central focus but also supports students, Fellows and academic visitors and researchers in disciplines related to identified elements of human welfare. These disciplines include business studies, criminology, education, economics, environment, forestry and natural resources, ethics, media and information studies, medical history, refugee studies, and social studies.

The current Warden, Sir John Hanson, previously Director General of the British Council (Plate 59, p. 157), encouraged the maintenance of such diversity while actively seeking a stronger voice for Green College in University business and decision-making. Largely due to his work the Governing Body of the College and the Council of the University now recognize the value, status and needs of the College and the valuable role it plays in meeting targets of increasing student numbers. The current Vice-Warden, Professor John Sear, a practising anaesthetist, secured for the college a significant proportion of the clinical students entering under the graduate entry 'fast track' system; he was also instrumental in securing the Kawasaki Research Fellowship scheme with Kawasaki University in Japan.

These various increases in the student body and the Fellowship, plus the University's policy on increasing student numbers overall, dictated the recent development of plans for further expansion of the College. These plans provide for significantly more accommodation for students and visiting academics, more space for teaching, academic meetings, library facilities, information technology resources, and administration. The trends in numbers of students and Fellows have been progressively upward since the formation of the College but the additional expansion is needed for financial and political reasons; consequently there has been an increasing demand for administrative offices, domestic and academic accommodation and social facilities with parallel pressures on the Observatory.

The impacts of the College on the Radcliffe Observatory

By 1977, the Nuffield Institute for Medical Research had moved out of the Observatory and its associated buildings. The Observatory contained offices and various small laboratories, with an X-ray department in the west wing and the Department of Clinical Biochemistry in the east wing. None of these rooms and facilities met the needs of a college and a Buildings Committee was set up to begin the transformation; the furnishing and decoration was undertaken by Lady Doll in conjunction with Jack Lankester, the University Surveyor and Green College architect.

Lankester Quad was built during 1978-9 and the gates were opened to the first thirty students on 1 September 1979. The accommodation block (named the Doll Building but sometimes irreverently called the Doll's House by appreciative students) was built on the site of what had formerly been the Radcliffe Infirmary's animal house and was opened in 1981 a year after the opening of the newly furnished and decorated Observatory. During the 1980s, the ugly Lodge in the south-east corner of the College was replaced (after opposition from the Victorian Society and a public inquiry) by a new building containing extra student accommodation, a bookstack, storage rooms and an underground lecture theatre. The theatre accommodated a hundred persons and was named after Sir Edward Abraham whose E. P. Abraham Trust had provided substantial financial support. The building was opened in 1989, and was named after the second Warden, Sir (now Lord) John Walton, who had initiated the project and seen it through to completion.

In the Observatory, during the time of the Nuffield Institute for Medical Research (see Chapter 6), there had been offices, laboratories, alligators, many sheep and even a sword-swallower. Today the first floor of the tower contains the main dining room seating up to sixty people, a smaller dining room seating up to sixteen (named after Professor William Gibson who was instrumental in bringing Sir Richard Doll and Dr Cecil Green together) and a Fellows' Room that is often used for meetings of small committees. On the ground floor the Common Room now occupies what was originally the main entrance hall; it is entered from the north and the original, imposing, southern entrance is no longer used.

The west wing contains the kitchens and a music room, the east wing houses the library, and the Observer's House has now become student accommodation and offices; among these the Ida Green Room, at first converted into a seminar room, is now the Warden's office. The Observer's stables became the site of a small lecture theatre and the Pathology Museum from the beginning of the Medical School; under Green College they were converted to a bar and games room, and a small but frequently used art gallery.

These are the original buildings directly connected with the Observatory but Green College has added substantially to the built environment on the site. New facilities include the Doll Building for student accommodation, the main office block, guest quarters, computer room and front lodge alongside the Woodstock Road, the Fellowship House for offices and married students' accommodation in the front Lankester Quadrangle, and the Walton

Building in the McAlpine Quadrangle (named after the Robert McAlpine Construction Company that constructed the Walton Building and generously contributed to the costs). These, together with the magnificent gardens described in Chapter 3, set off the Observatory coherently in a modern environment that admirably portrays its classical origins and its neo-Georgian structure. It should not be forgotten too that Green College acquired the one large house in Observatory Street for the Warden's lodgings before the College was open and has progressively acquired small houses in the street for married student (or other) accommodation.

Students and the special case of Osler House

One of the primary aims of founding Green College was to provide clinical students with college facilities during their clinical training. The original Observer's House was, at the insistence of Lord Nuffield in the 1930s, known as Osler House. From some time during the Second World War, Osler House was taken over for two purposes; the first was to provide space for the administrative offices of the Medical School, and the second was to provide rooms for a social club and a small library for clinical students. Osler House Club was registered under the Licensing Act and recognized as an official University Club in 1948.

For over thirty years, while the Medical School was based in the Radcliffe Infirmary, Osler House was very popular. Students and medical staff would often meet at the bar to discuss medicine, and such rich sources of gossip as the idiosyncrasies of the consultants, the latest scandals, the final examinations, and which 'house jobs' were vacant. It may have been a narrow enclosed medical society, unleavened by contacts with graduate students in other disciplines, but few if any of the clinical students saw that as a disadvantage.

When Green College was founded, it was agreed in discussions with the Osler House Club that all members of Green College would automatically become members of the Club.

At first the new John Radcliffe Hospital provided no adequate facilities for medical students in its plans; there was an uncomfortable and very unpopular period for the members of the Club when the students had just one room in the John Radcliffe Hospital allotted to them. No one was happy about this and, with increasing numbers of clinical students, it was not possible to provide the type of facilities that had been available. On the initiative of Sir Richard Doll, however, the Chairman of the Oxford Area Health Authority, Lady McCarthy, agreed that Green College could buy a house (the Dower House adjoining the John Radcliffe Hospital) to which the Osler House Club could be moved. The new Osler House Club became as useful and popular as the original Club in the Observer's House and Sir John Walton, during his Wardenship, raised funds for a major extension of the Club' building.

There was, and still is, reciprocity between Green College and the new Osler House. Every graduate student at Green College has access to certain facilities at the new Osler House Club in Headington, and every clinical student has reciprocal rights in using some of the facilities of the college. Green College and Osler House have joint sports teams, and combined boat crews in races on the Isis; the College continues to finance some of the facilities of Osler House Club and joint social activities including Christmas and summer balls. This growing cooperation has also increased pressures on the College's resources.

Green College is a post-graduate college and all its students have first degrees and previous experience of other colleges or universities. The number of such mature clinical students who became members of the College steadily increased. About one quarter of all 125 clinical students admitted in 2004 were members of Green College. One notable change is that an increasing number of Cambridge students have come to the Oxford clinical school. In 1958 there were only four; now about one quarter of the clinical intake (approximately 30) come from Cambridge where Green College has a sister college, St Edmund's College.

In the academic year 2004-5, out of a total of 343 students in all disciplines, 93 (27 per cent) were reading clinical medicine; 147 (43 per cent) were engaged in research, mainly in health and the health sciences; 73 (21 per cent) were attending courses for an MSc or M Phil, including sociology and social policy (17), Geography and the Environment (17), Anthropology (16), Education (6), Development Studies (6), History of Medicine (6), Criminology (2), Forced Migration (2) and Diagnostic Imaging (1). In addition 15 pursued the Post Graduate Certificate in Education, 9 the Master of Business Administration course, and there were two on the Foreign Service Programme, two on 1-year diploma courses, and one Visiting Student. Prior to their degree ceremonies the students assemble for lunch and briefing by the Dean of Degrees in the Observatory. Sir Crispin Tickell established the series of public presentations by research students to each other, their supervisors and other College members; this was intended to assist in training them to disseminate their findings, a process that is now a common requirement of Research Councils and university departments.

Fellows, students, Common Room members, visitors and staff share the college's resources and there is no concept of a 'high table' for Fellows only. The student body makes up a virtual Middle Common Room (MCR) for cultural, social and sporting activities and for representing student views to the Warden and Governing Body. At any given time, the success of the MCR depends to a large extent on the energy and initiative of its President and Committee, and also on the encouragement of the Warden and Fellows. There have been periods of relative apathy but now the MCR is very lively and there is little if any split between medical and non-medical students. Furthermore, a network has grown up between the MCRs of colleges throughout the University; within that network, Green College has a reputation for exceptional friendliness and good facilities for social occasions.

It is a commonplace axiom, worth restating nevertheless, that the education of students includes not only the formal content of a syllabus or research programme, but also the collegiate contact, conversation, argument and exchange of ideas between students in a wide range of disciplines. It is what Oxford has always offered to undergraduates but only to a lesser extent to graduate students. In this respect Green College is now outstandingly successful. There are, as in many colleges, various societies, musical events in the Common Room, and an annual art exhibition of work by members of the College in the Stables Gallery. Current and former members gather at an annual "summer event" (Plate 60, p. 158).

The needs of Senior Members

When the College was founded, there were critics within and outside the University who said it would simply become an enclosed, narrow, medical society with little academic activity. It is true that, in the early days, the Fellowship consisted of a large majority from clinical medicine, and a minority recruited from administrative, social studies and bio-engineering. Bio-engineering was seen as increasingly important in medicine, and Fellowships (including Visiting Fellowships) were taken up by a number of people within that category. This was a subject close to the

heart of Dr Green, and Research Fellowships were provided by his former company, Texas Instruments.

The composition of the Governing Body Fellowship has changed according to the guidance of the mission statement of the college. The target proportion of clinical students and clinical Fellows is one third. In 2005 there were 46 Governing Body Fellows of whom 27 (59%) were involved in clinical or medically related subjects, 19 (41%) were working in fields not related directly to medicine. All Fellows, including some Emeritus Fellows, act as Academic Advisers to college students, independent of their technical advisers in the University's departments. In addition to social accommodation the Fellows use several small meeting rooms and a lecture theatre to meet their students and to provide public lectures and seminars that are a highly successful and notable feature of Green College.

Common Room membership increased, from 85 in 1979 to 148 in 1999 and had stabilized by 2005 as a policy decision at around 130. Most of the members use the social and sporting facilities of the college and many offer tutorials, lectures, seminars and special teaching for students of the college.

Research and Visiting Fellows

Like most colleges in Oxford, Green College provides Research Fellowships in a range of subjects related to its central mission; in 2005 there were 12 and these have been financed by a range of donor individuals and organizations. Generally these are for young post-doctoral workers in University departments; although they add to the usage of college resources they do not need office or laboratory space. In addition, however, many distinguished scientists and scholars wish to spend periods of sabbatical leave at the College as Visiting Fellows or Visiting Scholars and additional domestic and academic accommodation is desirable to meet their needs; the Rotunda (which was originally part of the Observatory) is specifically used by Visiting Fellows and Scholars as a quiet place to think, to read, or to write about their research.

Other initiatives and pressures at Green College

It is impossible in such a brief history to describe in any detail all the academic and social activities of college life. In addition to teaching for the students, there has been in each succeeding year a steady increase in the number of public lectures, seminars, and conferences held at the College. The Radcliffe Lecture, the Brian Walker Lecture, the Alan Emery Lecture and the four Green College Lectures in Hilary Term have become landmark events within the University, attracting distinguished speakers and such large audiences that they are held in the Witts Lecture Theatre of the Radcliffe Infirmary

In 1992, an important and novel link was established between the College and the Reuter Foundation Journalist Fellowship Programme, with the aim of encouraging understanding between the media on the one hand and medicine and science on the other. This resulted from a joint initiative of Neville Maxwell, the first Director of the Programme in Oxford when it was based in Queen Elizabeth House, Michael Nelson of the Reuter Foundation, who had been involved in the programme for some years, and Sir Crispin Tickell with Professor Burley in the College. The second Director of the Programme, Godfrey Hodgson, was elected a Fellow of the College, and the Journalist Fellows now become Visiting Scholars during their stay. Fellows write a research paper on a topic of their choosing and take part in a number of seminars and study trips. Through such contacts, they are provided with opportunities for taking part in the social, intellectual and cultural life of Oxford.

The Reuters Programme, now directed by Paddy Coulter, has its headquarters at 13 Norham Gardens, once the home of Sir William Osler, Regius Professor of Medicine in Oxford from 1904 to 1919. Number 13 was purchased for Green College in 2001 with the aid of a generous benefaction by Dr John P. McGovern MD, of Houston, Texas, Honorary Fellow of the College, who simultaneously endowed an Annual Lecture in the History of Medicine. The ground floor now houses the Osler-McGovern Centre, an excellent seminar centre comprising the entrance hall, Osler's drawing room and the study where Sir John Walton created a museum of Osler memorabilia; this is managed by the Friends of 13 Norham Gardens and visited by Osler admirers from all over the world. The Centre is well used by the Wellcome Unit for the History of Medicine and a range of other organizations.

In addition to the Reuter Programme, there is now a strategy for encouraging the development of specialized centres in Green College. They aim to encourage inter-disciplinary research and to complement, not replace, the work of University departments. It is partly because funding bodies prefer to support narrowly focused and highly specialized projects in departments that there is an obvious need for centres elsewhere that will involve collaboration between academics in different disciplines and departments. Not only can such college centres undertake research that would otherwise face great difficulty in attracting funding, but they can also provide a collegiate base for academic-related staff to whom University entitlement to college association is not available.

The first of these centres, founded in the same year as the Reuter Programme, was the Centre for Environmental Policy and Understanding. Recognizing the barrier between science and environmental thinking on the one hand, and politics, economics, policy formation and decision taking on the other, the Green College Centre was established under the directorship of Sir Crispin Tickell to bridge the gap between science and policy-making in matters of the environment. Scientists are not always adept at communicating outside their specialities and often dislike the inter-disciplinary approach. Those responsible for most of the decisions in society are often hazy about science, prone to take scientific information and environmental considerations out of context, and apt to give way to the urgent and trivial rather than the long-term and important. To deal with such problems, the Centre has a large advisory group, invites Visiting Fellows, arranges seminars, commissions papers, and publishes the work of the Centre. It also aims to influence educated public opinion through public presentations, articles in the press, and participation in radio and television programmes.

The second Green College initiative, established in 1999, was collaboration with Nihon University in Tokyo to study and compare health and social services for older people in Japan and the UK. This development has come about as the culmination of a three-year exploratory programme led by Dr Alex Gatherer and Professor Sir John Grimley Evans in Oxford, and Professor Yoshio Maya in Japan, with funding from a grant by the President of Nihon University. The intention was that this venture should broaden into a Green College Centre for a wider international collaboration concerned with comparative studies of systems of health and social services in developed countries.

The third initiative, also established in 1999, was the Green College Centre for Natural Resources and Development, financed for three years under the joint leadership of the current Warden, Sir John Hanson, and Professor Burley, then the Vice-Warden of the College. Collaborators in this centre came from such departments as the Oxford Forestry Institute, the Environmental Change Institute, the Wellcome Unit for the

History of Medicine, departments concerned with development overseas, and an interesting project named 'Global Initiatives for Traditional Systems of Health', led by Dr Gerard Bodeker, which has organized studies of anti-malarial therapy using traditional medicine and has provided world-wide policy leadership in relation to complementary and traditional medicine for the Commonwealth Ministers of Health.

The general purpose of all such initiatives is to encourage, through inter-disciplinary studies, the growth of Green College as an academic centre concerned with medicine, human welfare, and the environment. Collectively such activities bring credit to the University and college but do add to the pressures on available space and promote constant reconsideration of the design, use and furnishing of buildings including the Radcliffe Observatory.

Green College is clearly an academic unit of a prestigious university seeking primarily to meet the needs of its students, Fellows and academic visitors. However, the Governing Body has a commitment to the wider community, not only through charitable works but also by making some facilities open to individual and group visits, art exhibitions and concerts. The Observatory building itself has been used, for example, by the European Youth Baroque Training Orchestra and the Richard Colburn Quartet; the garden is frequently open to the public for charitable fund-raising. The Gallery is also available to non-members for public exhibitions of art, photography, pottery and sculpture. The Radcliffe Observatory itself is opened to the public occasionally throughout the year.

Through constant familiarity it is easy for Green College members to overlook the enormous influence of Wyatt's magnificent Observatory on the character of the college. Although the college lies between the arterial traffic of Woodstock Road and Walton Street, on a warm summer evening when the surrounding buildings seem to reflect away the noise of cars, it can be extraordinarily quiet and peaceful in the gardens beneath the beautiful Tower of the Winds. It was by singular good fortune that the Observatory was vacant and neglected just at the time when Sir Richard Doll had the vision, energy and courteous perseverance to create a college in which medicine and health sciences play a central role. Now those charged with the governance of the college and the maintenance of its fabric face the increasing demands to utilize buildings efficiently and seek to expand the resources while maintaining the essential historic character of the Radcliffe Observatory.

Plate 54. Sir Richard Doll, First Warden, 1979–83

Plate 55. Drs Cecil and Ida Green, Founding Benefactors of Green College

Plate 56. Sir John (now Lord) Walton of Detchant, Warden, 1983-9

Plate 57. Dr Trevor Hughes, Acting Warden, 1989-90

Plate 58. Sir Crispin Tickell, Warden, 1990-7

Plate 59. Sir John Hanson, Warden, 1998 – present

Plate 60. HRH Princess Anne with students at the College garden party, 1999

Plate 61. HRH Princess Anne with Sir Richard Doll and Sir John Hanson

Chapter 8

The Conservation of the Exterior of the Radcliffe Observatory

Peter Inskip

The Radcliffe Observatory received its share of attention in the famous campaigns of the 1960s and 1970s to restore Oxford's crumbling stone, the need for which was already apparent on so many buildings in late nineteenth-century photographs when the problem was already recognized. Indeed, the repair of Oxford's stonework had already progressed with the replacement in 1868 of the array of the so-called Emperors' Heads outside the Sheldonian Theatre which had been made two hundred years before. Only a hundred years later, the erosion of the stone was seen as justification for their replacement yet again in 1970-2.[1] The scale of the refacing of buildings in Oxford that was carried out at that period was massive and it meant that much of the historic fabric of the City was lost. Thirty years later, the degree of the intervention has to be questioned and in the first two phases of the present campaign of repairs at the Observatory a much more conservative approach to the masonry has been taken with the view to retaining as much of the original stonework as is possible.

The Observatory was repaired in 1960-9 under Marshall Sisson, RA,[2] a sensitive architect, well-known for his reconstruction after war damage of St John's, Smith Square,

and, like Keene, Surveyor to Westminster Abbey. Using Weldon stone, he refaced the majority of the south elevation up to the level of the balustrade at the head of the first floor and the wings completely. Regrettably, the latter included carrying the stone across the original telescope slots. These utilitarian elements had been carefully integrated into the design by locating them adjacent to the internal angles created by the articulation of the bays at each end. Their removal disturbed the symmetries of the wings and it is hoped that they will be restored when funds are available (Plate 62, p. 168). The radiused north elevation, however, was left by Sisson and it also appears that a restriction on funds contained the replacement of stone at high level to the more accessible areas of the tower which could be reached from the flat lead roofs of the lower storeys.

The recovery of the status of the Radcliffe Observatory as a landmark and the precision of Wyatt's building were two important issues that needed to be addressed in the recent conservation project carried out under the direction of Peter Inskip + Peter Jenkins Architects. The first process was to clean the building using specialized conservation cleaning methods. This was necessary to remove the thick crusts of sulphation caused by dissipation of air pollution in rainwater converting limestone to gypsum on the surface. Aside from their unsightly appearance, these thick black deposits also cause physical damage to the stone below and accelerate the process of decay. Even relatively less destructive surface soiling can clog the pores of the stone and set further processes of deterioration in motion. Instead of the harsh abrasive regimes employed in the past that would often destroy the surface of the stone and hasten resoiling, a range of cleaning methods has been used following extensive on-site trials and research. In the end several different methods were adopted depending upon location and nature of the material to be cleaned. Most of the stonework was cleaned using two proprietary systems: 'Doff' steam cleaning was used to provide an initial clean to the stonework followed by 'Flirok', a dry micro air abrasive system, which was used at low pressure to remove residual hard sulphation crusts which had built up on sheltered mouldings and carved detail. The bas-relief panels of the Winds were also given an initial clean using the Doff system, but because of their fragile condition this was followed by further cleaning to residual soiling using poultices and mechanically picking off the softened crust with scalpels.

Several different methods were found to be appropriate for cleaning each of the Coade stone elements depending upon their condition and design. Methods included hand washing, micro abrasive (wet and dry), and chemical poultices. Great care was taken to ensure no damage occurred to the 'fireskin', a protective layer of vitrified ceramic formed during firing of the clay. The surface was examined before and after cleaning trials by touch and 30x magnification. Where chemical poultices were used, the pH was monitored before, during and after cleaning to ensure the chemicals had been completely neutralized (Plate 63, p. 169).

Given that many quarries are now worked out, the stone had to be chosen to ensure both a visual match and that its weathering characteristics were appropriate for the location where it was to be used on the building. Graham Lott of the British Geological Society advised on the suitability of replacements for the Windrush freestone from the geological unit known as the Taynton Limestone Foundation which had been used for the ashlar work, and the architects selected Syreford limestone from Cotswold Stone Quarries for the current repairs as an appropriate geological match.

It is now recognized that the design of the lime mortar is also as important as the stone itself. Samples of the original lime mortar were desegregated to allow a matching mortar to be achieved that would meet both physical and visual requirements. Mortars were required for both the pointing and conservation repairs to the stones themselves, particularly the sculpted bas-reliefs. The colour of a mortar is determined by its constituent sands, invariably based in the eighteenth century on those local to the site to limit transportation costs, and a palette of colours was derived to match the variations found in the carved stones.

The recent campaign of repairs has been restricted by the budget to items of the greatest urgency which were placing the building at risk coupled with repairs that were commensurate with the artistic value of the building. The work has focused primarily on the high level areas that had not been available to Sisson. Wholesale replacement of individual stones was kept to a minimum with preference given to cutting out small eroded sections of a stone and 'indenting' with a new piece in order to re-establish weatherings. Where whole stones or indents were introduced the general intention was to re-instate the original profiles, not the later interventions.

In certain areas, such as window sills, replacement stone was necessary. The most serious problem encountered has been with the plinths of the balustrades where water, trapped by lead flashings introduced after the War, has not allowed the stone to breathe and dry out, and the consequential decay has necessitated the dismantling and rebuilding of the balustrade above a new plinth course. The plinth course had been largely replaced during the previous restoration regime resulting in the alteration or complete loss of the original moulded detail. By careful examination of the few remaining original profiles it was possible to reinstate the plinth course to its original design.

The repair of both the carved and plain stonework also required a level of aesthetic judgment if one was to make sense of Wyatt's crisp neo-classical elevations. For example, with the windows of the Observation Room, if a missing volute disrupted the legibility of the Corinthian capital then it was important to piece-in a replacement with a new carved stone volute. However, if the erosion of another element, such as an acanthus leaf, did not interfere with the reading of the same capital, given its overall context and height in the building, then it was appropriate to simply cap it with mortar to eliminate 'water traps' where stone erosion could allow water to pool and cause further damage (Plate 65, p. 170). Such an approach also applied to the base of the cornice: fully eroded modillions were replaced with new stone carved to the original profile, rather than the abstracted, simplified form used in the 1960s campaign, whilst the damaged flowers in the coffers between them were simply capped with mortar to prolong the life of the surviving stone (Plate 64, p. 169).

Erosion of soft beds in the stone had also caused the loss of the complete face of the Ionic capitals belonging to the pair of engaged pilasters at the external angles on the south elevation of the main block. Not only was the decay entraining water into the wall, but the eroded stone capitals contrasted severely with the largely pristine condition of the neighbouring Coade stone capitals which had retained all their fine detail. Both of the pilasters were narrower than the others, and those at the corner returned on the sides of the building and were 'handed' in opposite directions; they would have needed to have been specially cast as individual pieces and it is assumed that they were carved in stone rather than making two special moulds for casting in artificial stone to spare some expense. The current replacements were carved in stone by Corin Johnson.

James Wyatt had used Coade's artificial stone for the capitals on the pilasters at Heaton Hall in 1772, only three years after Mrs Coade had established her manufactory at Lambeth.[3] It was, therefore, logical that his beautifully detailed Ionic capitals on the Radcliffe Observatory should continue this practice. In Oxford, he extended the use of this patented material to other architectural details. It is likely that the guilloche string course that extends out to the head of the wings was originally in Coade stone as it matches the castings used at John Wesley's house in City Road, London, that were supplied by Mrs Coade. However, this was replaced in carved stone in the 1960s. The more ornamental details used on the elevations, such as the paterae and garlanded tablets, are standard items taken from Coade's catalogues that were also extensively used by Robert Adam and, later, by John Soane. The large paterae that appear on the Radcliffe Observatory are illustrated in Coade's 1784 catalogue, at a cost of $2\frac{1}{2}$ guineas each, but they are centred on a daisy-like feature instead of the engraved head; another plate of 1778 includes the garlanded plaques (Plate 66, p. 171).

At Heaton, the plaques on the garden side of the house had been made of stone, but they were not very well carved. Since both James Wyatt and his brother, Samuel, were to use Coade plaques extensively, it is possible that, in the light of this experience, they had suggested that Eleanor Coade should make something of the kind when there was an opportunity. The Radcliffe Observatory provided such a project. The Signs of the Zodiac and the larger rectangular panels symbolizing the Times of Day: Morning, Noon, and Evening, were designed by J. C. F Rossi, RA.[4] Four of the twelve panels are listed in Mrs Coade's catalogue of 1784, suggesting that the Zodiac panels were made well into the 1780s with no rush, given the long building history of the Observatory. Rossi was a popular sculptor, carving the colossal lions for the western Watergate at Somerset House and the model for the Coade stone caryatids at St Pancras Church, but his work was dismissed by Flaxman as 'mason's work rather than that of a sculptor'.[5] The plaques at the Observatory exemplify his frequent collaborations with Mrs Coade (Plates 17-22, pp. 28-29).

Much of the Coade stone was in relatively good condition and had faired far better than the surrounding stonework. Due to the nature of ceramics with all of the variables that can be inadvertently altered during its making, including the mixture of the clay, the placement in the kiln and the length of firing, it is inevitable that some of the Coade stone pieces are more durable than others. Where the protective 'fireskin' had broken down the softer core was exposed and the surface had become friable. It was reconsolidated using specially matched hydraulic lime mortars and in a few carefully selected locations 'Wacker OH', a proprietary chemical consolidant, was used after tests. Small fractures had occurred in much of the Coade due to normal shrinkage and expansion. This is another reason why removal of the soiling was important as the dark surface can attract a greater level of heat from the sun causing increased thermal expansion. This is especially problematic in winter when rapid cooling may follow, exacerbating the situation. Cracks may also occur in architec-

tural terracotta due to rusting of ferrous cramps used as fixings. This was not found to be a problem at the Observatory and in the few locations where iron fixings were exposed and found to be in good condition, a rust inhibitor was applied and the fixings reconcealed. In instances where repair to surrounding stonework exposed cramps, these were removed and replaced with stainless steel. Cracks were filled to ensure there would be no further water penetration and deterioration, using a thin slurry of hydraulic lime injected with syringes.

The publication of Stuart and Revett's *The Antiquities of Athens* had as profound an effect on sculptors as it had on architects. John Flaxman's memorial to Mrs Morley in Gloucester Cathedral of 1784[6] develops his design for the supporting angels from Revett's engravings of the bas-reliefs on the Tower of the Winds (Plate 67, p. 171). The same publication was still providing a similar influence in 1820-4 when Schinkel adorned the four corner towers of Schloss Tegel with bas-reliefs of the wind gods which closely follow the details shown in the engravings in the first volume.[7] For his client, Humboldt, the Greek myths personified forces in nature, making visible and knowable the larger forces of the world and the four corner towers, orientated to the four cardinal points of the compass, reflected those forces (Plate 68, p. 172).

The versions of the Winds by John Bacon RA[8] at the Observatory are nearly ten years later than the memorial to Mrs Morley and were carved in 1792-4. Bacon was also connected to Mrs Coade and her manufactory as she appointed him superintendent of the works in 1771, and he was responsible for many of the company's designs working in parallel with Rossi.[9] Bacon was, however, a much better sculptor than Rossi, and while Rossi was supplying supporting sculptures for Somerset House, he was responsible for the principal statuary groups such as the bronze of

King George III and the River Thames. Similarly, it was John Bacon who was responsible for the main statuary at the Radcliffe Observatory. Even if he was exalted, Bacon was always concerned by the criticism that he received claiming that he had no real knowledge of the antique and it was probably because of this that his transcription of each Wind is very close to the contemporary engravings. The carvings themselves were executed as bas-reliefs and jointing of the stone suggests that much of the work was finished *in situ*. Each of the Winds is identified with beautiful cast brass Greek letters set on the string course below each figure. These were cleaned with lemon juice and coated with 'Incralac' to maintain their appearance. With the building being orientated exactly on an east west axis, the names correspond to each face of the building.

Considerable erosion had occurred to the sculptures of the Winds facing the prevailing wind from the south west. As a result, the decayed reliefs of the South West Wind and the West Wind that could be reached from the roof of the main block had been completely replaced with new carvings forty years ago. However successful the new reliefs are, a copy is no substitute for an original work of art, and it was important that the approach taken in the recent campaign should focus on conservative repairs designed both to maintain the original fabric and to reveal the quality of the sculpture. This was achieved through the judicious piecing in of small scale stone repairs in seriously eroded areas supplemented with the use of lime mortar repairs built up on stainless steel armatures. The latter not only eliminated water traps, but were also concerned with the integration of the new stonework with the original carving. One thus had the stone carver working in parallel with the conservator. To recover the legibility of the sculpture, where its form had been lost through the differential erosion of the individual, small-scale, stone blocks from which the bas-relief was carved, the missing detail was remodelled *in situ* in clay, with reference to the eighteenth-century engravings of the antique carvings that had guided Bacon (Plate 69, p. 172). This was crucial to the understanding of the eroded limbs, amphora, and the more diaphanous draperies that the original sculptor had carved so successfully. The process was one of discussion and collaboration between the stone carver, Richard Noviss, the conservator, Alex Carrington, and the architects, reviewing the progress as the clay model proceeded. Once the work was agreed, it was recorded with plaster casts which were subsequently used to guide the final stone carving which was carried out again *in situ* on blocks of indented stone (Plate 70, p. 173).

Citing the pineapple surmounting the dome of the Mausoleum of Hadrian, and the triton holding in his hand a wand on the roof of the Tower of the Winds, Sir John Soane had noted in his Royal Academy lectures of 1812 that 'these are the only kinds of ornament the ancients admitted on the exterior of their domes. In modern works the external simple and beautiful figure of the dome is sometimes destroyed by improper decoration', and that roofs needed to be 'terminated with light appropriate ornaments, as in ancient works'.[10]

The very beautiful lead statues of Herakles and Atlas that surmount the roof were devised in c.1784 and are also by John Bacon. They follow the tradition of the Farnese Atlas, but with two figures (Plate 71, p. 174). He united them with a great globe bearing on its base an inscription which Christopher Hussey noted in 1930 gave the names of 'James Wyatt, Esq., architect; John Bacon Esq. RA, sculptor; James Pears Esq., Mayor of Oxford, builder; John Hudson, clerk of the works; Henry Barker, measurer; and John Dixon, clerk to James Wyatt.'[11] It was Dixon who made the beautiful drawing of the

Observatory which adorned the *Oxford Almanack* of 1794 (Plate 35, p. 59). The early engravings of the completed building show that the globe was marked with terrestrial lines, extending from the poles which protrude on the axis of the world, with equatorial and longitudinal lines at right angles to them (Plate 32, p. 57). A contemporary example of a similar globe with applied terrestial markings was to be found on the Memorial to Captain Cook at Stowe erected in 1778, and earlier examples are at Greenwich Hospital, where terrestrial and celestial globes were mounted on the main gatepiers in the first half of the century.

The *Country Life* photographs accompanying Hussey's article indicate that the globe had already been altered by 1930 as the terrestrial lining had been replaced with thick painted lines that simply followed the horizontal arrangement of the segments of the sheets that made up the globe. Despite their still being in place, the lining no longer bore any relationship with the protruding poles which had generated the original dynamic markings (Plate 72, p. 175). On the evidence of other contemporary sculptures, one would anticipate that the original globe would have been of lead, but Hussey describes it as copper. This cannot be taken necessarily as being definitive since he mistakenly states that the lead figures are made of cast iron in the same article. However, copper could have been possible in the 1790s as it would have been in line with the interest in its use as a building material that became apparent in the last quarter of the eighteenth century.[12] That it was of a different material from the figures would not have been of major consequence as the whole group was unified with stone coloured paint.[13]

A new, unpainted copper globe was provided in the 1970s as part of the roof repairs carried out by Messrs Norman and Underwood (Plate 73, p. 175).[14] Its segments were again joined horizontally and the polar projections were re-incorporated. However, it appeared to be completely weightless, and such was the effect that the figures looked more as if they were restraining a balloon from drifting away than supporting the weight of the World – the polar projection at the base in fact appearing to provide the point for inflation. To a modern eye, it had been referred more to the film industry than mythology, recalling Adenoid Hynkel in Chaplin's *Great Dictator* of 1941 progressing from struggling to support the World to then playing with it as easily as an inflated balloon (Plate 74, p. 175).

An extensive layer of sulphation had accumulated on parts of the figures and these were removed with careful hand cleaning to arrest corrosion of the lead. What appeared like small barnacles had accumulated on the surface of the lead. These were found to be formed from the deterioration of previous layers of paint and were removed during the cleaning process. The sculptures were generally in a good state of repair but small holes and cracks had formed. It was necessary to fill these as they would eventually become enlarged and lead to much more serious damage. It was important to ensure that the core and armature of the lead statues remained sealed from the weather, particularly in such an exposed position atop the Observatory. The sculptures and globe were painted in lead paint matching the stone coloured limewash in order to restore the group to their original aesthetically cohesive state. The surface was first cleaned with a neutral pH soap then lightly scoured using micro abrasive and finally a proprietary etch primer was applied to create a suitable surface for painting.

The restoration of the lining on the globe had not been included in the scope of works as it did not affect its condition. However, Stephen Gee, the project architect, and the writer kept feeling that it would be a serious mistake not to carry out this work, even if it was not in the category of urgent works. It was the end of the project and the scaffold was about to be taken down so access would not be available again for some time. With the cooperation of a very imaginative contractor, Fred Markland of E. Bowman and Son of Stamford, the lining was reinstated in copper lightning conductor tapes marking out the longitudinal lines radiating from the poles and crossed at right angles with the equator and tropics. The problem of not being able to afford the gilding on the equator was resolved by the architects carrying it out themselves in a god-sent interval between heavy showers on a Sunday, the day before the scaffolding was dismantled.[15] Not only has the restoration of the globe reinstated the integrity of the statuary group, so that the whole reads as one sculpture, but it has restored the iconographic programme of the Observatory through reuniting the Herakles and Atlas group visually with the Winds and the Signs of the Zodiac.

Finally, the stonework was given five coats of limewash, a material that still allows the underlying stone to be understood and gradually weathers to unite with the masonry (Plate 15, p. 26). The use of limewash was characteristic of most stone and brick buildings throughout the whole of the extended eighteenth century, providing a protective coating to the masonry as well as unifying disparate materials: different stones, plasters and renders.[16] The Observatory was no exception. Microscopic paint analysis carried out by Catherine Hassall of samples surviving in sheltered areas of the elevations demonstrated that the stonework had been limewashed when it was completed and the practice had continued well into the nineteenth century.[17] Examination at 500x magnification allowed the reconstruction of the original colour with earth pigments mixed into the basic white limewash. The decoration of the lead statuary was confirmed by a similar exercise which also established the greyed-white colour for the windows. In addition, it indicated that the fanlights over the doors in the wings were originally grained as mahogany to match the doors below, and that it was possible that at one stage the windows were grained as oak, matching their internal decoration. The limewash holds the light and responds to weather conditions in ever-varying ways. It has played a key role in reinstating the Radcliffe Observatory as the landmark in the fabric of the city that it was intended to be by James Wyatt, and it has reinforced the building as the focus of Green College two hundred years later (Plates 75 and 76, p. 176).

Appendix to Chapter 8

Consultants and Craftsmen involved in the Repairs

Architects	Peter Inskip + Peter Jenkins Architects: Peter Inskip, Director; Stephen Gee, Project Architect; Michelle Hedges, Architectural Conservation Assistant
Structural engineer	Ralph Mills
Quantity surveyor	Gordon Cain
Paint analyst	Catherine Hassall
Contractor	E. Bowman and Sons: Fred Markland, Conservation Manager; Tony Davidson, Foreman; Alex Carrington, Conservator; Bob Morris, Stone Mason; Darren Tuddutt, Stone Mason; Kay Fentante, Assistant Conservator; Allen Haughton, Steve Wooding and Dave Perkins, Joiners
Stone carvers	Richard Noviss (Winds), Corin Johnson (architectural details)
Lead Conservator	Rupert Harris
Stone cleaning	Kimbolton Restoration: Matt Wright, Simon Linnell, Adam Barber
Brass letters repairs	Mid Beds Locksmiths: Andy Burr

NOTES

1. Oakeshott, W. F. (Ed.) (1975) *Oxford Stone Restored*. Oxford University Press, Oxford.
2. Oakeshott, W. F. (1975) 34-5.
3. The details on Coade are based on Kelly, A. (1990) *Mrs Coade's Stone*. Self-Publishing Association, Worcester.
4. For Rossi, see Gunnis (1968) *Dictionary of British Sculptors 1660-1851*. Abbey Library, London. 326-9.
5. Gunnis (1968) 326.
6. Whinney, M. (1964) *Pelican History of Art: Sculpture in Britain 1530-1830*. Penguin Books, London. Plate 244.
7. Bergdoll, B. (1994) *Karl Friedrich Schinkel, an Architecture for Prussia*. Rizzoli, New York. Plate 56.
8. For Bacon, see Gunnis (1968) 24-8, and Chapter 2 this volume.
9. Kelly (1990) 40-6.
10. Soane (1812) R.A. Lecture VI. Quoted in Watkin, D. (1996) *Sir John Soane, Enlightenment, Thought and the Royal Academy Lectures*. Cambridge University Press, Cambridge. 569.
11. Hussey, C. (1930) The Radcliffe Observatory. *Country Life*. 10 May 1930. 67: 674-81.
12. The Stowe building accounts in the Huntington Library, Pasadena, show that copper was used as a roofing material on the service wings of Stowe House and on Stowe Church, Buckinghamshire, in the last decade of the eighteenth century.
13. S. Gee examination paint analysis.
14. Norman & Underwood accounts (Green College).
15. Michelle Hedges and Peter Inskip executed the gilding.
16. Observation based on paint analysis of various buildings at Stowe, Buckinghamshire, Moggerhanger, Bedfordshire, and in London.
17. Hassall, C. (2004) *Examination of Paint Samples from the Radcliffe Observatory*. Unpublished report for Green College.

Plate 62. The Radcliffe Observatory 1930. The slots for the meridian instruments are visible in the break in the parapet of the west wing (*Country Life Picture Library*)

Plate 63. Chemical cleaning being undertaken

Plate 64. Damaged flowers capped with mortar

Plate 65. Corinthian capitals before and after cleaning

Plate 66. A page from the Coade catalogue 1778

Plate 67. Mrs Morley's Memorial, Gloucester Cathedral

Plate 68. Bas-reliefs of the Wind gods on Schloss Tegel

Plate 69. Notos, from J. Stuart and N. Revett, *The Antiquities of Athens*, 1762-1830

Plate 70. Six stages in the restoration of Notos at the Radcliffe Observatory

Plate 71. Herakles and Atlas before and after restoration

Plate 72. Herakles, Atlas and the Globe showing the painted lines following the segments of the Globe (*Country Life Picture Library*)

Plate 73. Herakles, Atlas and the Globe in the 1970s

Plate 74. Charlie Chaplin as Adenoid Hynkel in *The Great Dictator*

Plate 75. The Tower of the Winds from Walton Street, Oxford

Plate 76. The Tower of the Winds from the Lankester Quadrangle of Green College

Select Bibliography

Ackermann, R. (1814) *History of the University of Oxford*. London.

Beeching, N. (1978) Illustrations of the Observatory. *Oxford Medical School Gazette*. XXX: 3: 54-9.

Betjemann, J. and Vaisey, D. (1971) *Victorian and Edwardian Oxford from Old Photographs*. B.T. Batsford Ltd, London.

Brewer, E. C. (1984) *Dictionary of Phrase and Fable*. Constable, London.

Brockliss, L. W. B. (1997) The European university in the age of revolution 1789-1850. In Brock, M. G. and Curthoys, M. C. (Eds) *The History of the University of Oxford* VI: *Nineteenth-Century Oxford*. Part 1. Clarendon Press, Oxford.

Chambers (1984) *Chambers Biographical Dictionary*. Revised edition. Chambers, Edinburgh.

Chapman, A. (1993) James Bradley, 1693-1762: an Oxford astronomer in eclipse. *Oxford Magazine*. Fourth Week, Trinity term. 17-19.

Chapman, A. (1993) Pure research and practical teaching: the astronomical career of James Bradley, 1693-1762. *Notes and Records of the Royal Society of London*. 47: 2.

Chapman, A. (2000) Thomas Hornsby and the Radcliffe Observatory. In: Fauvel, J., Flood, R. and Wilson, R. (Eds), *Oxford Figures: 800 years of the Mathematical Sciences*. Oxford University Press, Oxford.

Colvin, H. (1995) *Biographical Dictionary of British Architects 1600-1840*. Yale University Press, New Haven and London.

COS. *The Universal British Directory 1790-98*. Centre for Oxfordshire Studies, Oxford.

Cox, G.V. (1868) *Recollections of Oxford*. Macmillan, London.

Crossley, A. (ed.) (1979) *A History of the County of Oxford*. Volume IV *The City of Oxford*. Oxford University Press, Oxford.

Dale, A. (1956) *James Wyatt*. Basil Blackwell, Oxford.

Doll, R. (1982) Green College, Oxford: its contribution to clinical medicine. *British Medical Journal*. 285: 1805-6.

Donnelly, M. C. (1973) *A Short History of Observatories*. University of Oregon Books, Eugene, Oregon.

Dunkin, E. (1879) Rev. Robert Main. In *Obituary Notices of Astronomers*. Royal Astronomical Society, London.

Esdaile, K. (1930) The Radcliffe Observatory. *Journal of the Royal Society of Arts*. LXXVIII: 755-9.

Fauvel, J., Flood, R. and Wilson, R. (Eds) (2000) *Oxford Figures: 800 Years of the Mathematical Sciences*. Oxford University Press, Oxford.

Gray, A. S. (1958) The Radcliffe Observatory, *Oxford Medical School Gazette.* 10: 69.

Guest, I. (1991) *John Radcliffe and his Trust.* The Radcliffe Trust, London.

Hall, J. (1974) *Dictionary of Subjects and Symbols in Art.* John Murray Publishers Ltd, London.

Harrison, C. (Ed.) (1998) *John Malchair of Oxford.* Ashmolean Museum, Oxford.

Hibbert, C. and Hibbert, E. (Eds) (1988) *The Encyclopaedia of Oxford.* Macmillan, London.

Hinchcliffe, T. (1992) *North Oxford.* Yale University Press, New Haven and London.

Hussey, C. (1930) The Radcliffe Observatory, Oxford. *Country Life.* 10 May 1930. 67: 674-81.

Hutchins, R. (forthcoming 2006) *British University Observatories c.1820-1939.* Ashgate Publishing Ltd, Hampshire.

Lehman, R. (1974) The Radcliffe Observatory. *Oxford Medical School Gazette.* 23.

Mas, J. B. (Ed.) (1918) *Dr John Radcliffe, a Sketch of his Life with an Account of his Fellows and Foundations etc.* Clarendon Press, Oxford.

Oakeshott, W. F. (Ed.), photos by J. W. Thomas (1975) *Oxford Stone Restored: the Work of the Oxford Historic Buildings Fund 1957-1974.* Oxford University Press, Oxford.

Oxford Dictionary of National Biography (2004) Oxford University Press, Oxford.

Prest, J. (Ed.) (1993) *The Illustrated History of Oxford University.* Oxford University Press, Oxford and New York.

Rambaut, A. A. (1918) The Radcliffe Observatory. In Nias, J. B. (Ed.) *Dr John Radcliffe, a Sketch of his Life with an Account of his Fellows and Foundations etc.* Clarendon Press, Oxford. 117-23.

Selby-Green, J. (1990) *The History of the Radcliffe Infirmary.* Image Publications, Banbury, Oxon.

Sherwood, J. and Pevsner, N. (1974) *The Buildings of England: Oxfordshire,* Penguin, Harmondsworth.

Simcock, A. V. (1984) *The Ashmolean Museum and Oxford Science 1683-1983.* Oxford Museum of the History of Science, Oxford.

Smith, C. G. (1985) Meteorological observations at the Radcliffe Observatory. *Oxford Bulletin Scientific Instrument Society.* 5: 11-13.

Stuart, J. and Revett, N. (1762-1830) *The Antiquities of Athens: Measured and Delineated.* 5 vols. London (J. Haberkorn *et al.*).

Stone, L. (Ed.) (1974) *Oxford and Cambridge from the Fourteenth to the Early Nineteenth Century.* Princeton University Press, Princeton NJ.

Sutherland, L. S. and Mitchell, L. G. (Eds) (1986) *The History of the University of Oxford. V The Eighteenth Century.* Oxford University Press, Oxford.

Thackeray, A. D. (1972) *The Radcliffe Observatory: bi-centenary 1772-1972.* The Radcliffe Trust, London.

Tyack, G. (1998) *Oxford: an Architectural Guide.* Oxford University Press, Oxford and New York.

Tyack, G. (2000) The making of the Radcliffe Observatory. *The Georgian Group Journal,* X. 122-40.

Wallace, J. G. (1997) *Meteorological Observations at the Radcliffe Observatory Oxford: 1815-1995.* School of Geography, Oxford. Research Paper 53.

Ward, W. R. (1965) *Victorian Oxford.* Frank Cass & Co. Ltd, London.

Index